A LAYM[A]
LOOKS
PHILOSOPHY
- and a little science

To my wife, Dorothy, for her
continuing help and support in all matters

[1] Cyril Tomkins is Emeritus Professor of Business Finance and a previous Pro-Vice Chancellor of the University of Bath. He has published extensively in his own academic field, but this is the first time he has ventured into this one and so he sees himself very much as a layman in this field.

A LAYMAN LOOKS AT PHILOSOPHY

- and a little science

CYRIL TOMKINS[1]

BROWN DOG BOOKS

Published under licence by Brown Dog Books and
The Self-Publishing Partnership Ltd, 10b Greenway Farm, Bath Rd, Wick, nr.
Bath BS30 5RL

www.selfpublishingpartnership.co.uk

ISBN printed book: 978-1-83952-321-2
ISBN e-book: 978-1-83952-322-9

Cover design by Kevin Rylands
Internal design by Tim Jollands

Printed and bound in the UK

This book is printed on FSC certified paper

Contents

Foreword

The major part of this text was written in late 2014 and early 2015 during a period of medically enforced rest. Events have occurred since then which made me want to add further comments, but I did nothing about it until another period of enforced restriction of movement, this time due to Government advice to stay at home, protect the NHS and save lives due to the coronavirus crisis. Hence, one could argue that occasional enforced rests may do some good in-so-far as they encourage one to stop and think and set some thoughts down on paper.

Despite a six-year lapse between my first draft and the current time, I have not explored much philosophical literature in the interim. The text still relies heavily on Kenny's four volumes referenced in the Introduction and just a few more philosophical references and popularising science texts that I have since read. While I hope to get these notes published, as explained in the Introduction, they were initially written mostly to aid my own introspection and satisfaction as well, perhaps, as giving members of my family more insight as to who I am.

A relevant question is whether there is a wider community that might like to read this. First, some might like to pursue the route that I have taken in this text for the same reason that I have and explore their own views on these areas of philosophy and associated behaviour. In addition, however, and despite my very limited background in both philosophy and science, I make some suggestions for further thought. I stress, for example, why I now think there is a need to make a clear distinction between God[2] and religion and what agnosticism should mean. Also various suggestions are made relating to concepts such as evolution and teleological[3] inputs, competition, collaboration, consciousness, personal identity, ethics, political philosophy,

---

[2] To avoid complexity of phrasing, I have, throughout this text, referred to both God and the species Man with the masculine 'He'. This is not meant to imply that 'she' is any less relevant nor, indeed, that any attribution of sex is relevant when discussing God or Man.

[3] Teleology is explained in Section 2.

innovation, aesthetics and language. In particular, I conclude on the need to bring together these philosophical sub-fields to understand how they affect each other and lead to a more general systems thinking about how life and society evolves.

As the title of this text states, I do recognise that I am very much a layman in the areas covered. A layman in the study of philosophy, but also a layman in the areas of science addressed. The question is: can a layman, with limited knowledge of the subjects considered, still gain personal benefit from thinking about them? Of course he can. But can such a layman contribute new ideas by attempting to understand these areas and their significance? It will be for professionals in both science and philosophy, unlike me, to consider whether any of this is useful. At least I can say that I have enjoyed the process, clarified my own thoughts about these issues and contributed to my own knowledge, but I hope that it does a little more than that.

Easter, 2021

1.

Introduction

I have always had a passing interest in philosophy. It would be more correct to say that I have occasionally been interested in reading about some of the great philosophers in works summarising their views rather than studying those philosophers' original texts. I, therefore, state very clearly at the outset of this text that I am not a student of philosophy. I am merely an inadequately informed layman in the subject and, although I have had an academic career, I am certainly no academic expert on *any* of the dimensions of this discipline. I have not attempted to study in depth or academically the many intricacies of argument within the different themes in philosophy, for instance in logic and language. Nevertheless, having recently read through Anthony Kenny's four volumes *A New History of Western Philosophy*,[4] I came to the view that *any person* has a set of 'philosophies' that defines who they are and influences their lives. These may well usually be in the form of tacit assumptions, but, even without academic study, does not *everyone* act as though they have views on many of the themes covered in academic tomes on philosophy? The knowledge possessed and experience gained by each person will condition what philosophies they hold. Views held may well be quite uninformed and, hence, superficial or simplistic, but do not we *all*, even those without much education, behave in accordance with fairly consistent attitudes towards topics like metaphysics, physical science, ethics, political philosophy, aesthetics, religion and logic? Many may not be very familiar with such terminology, but surely all human beings have at least *their own* intuitive understanding of the world we live in, what it means *for them* to be alive and have a worthwhile life, what political stance *they* take and why, what *they* admire as beautiful or how *they* should behave from a moral perspective.

---

[4] Anthony Kenny, *A New History of Western Philosophy*, volumes 1 to 4, Oxford University Press, 2004 to 2007.

Of course, even if we have not studied the arguments of the great philosophers, our attitudes will be influenced by them as they have filtered down through society through discussion and direction by those with power to influence[5]. But what has filtered down to each of us individually? What do we take as given in the form of 'philosophies' as we carry out our daily lives? Clearly, there will be large variations from person to person and group to group and, indeed, variations over time possessed by each individual as our knowledge and experience changes. This is obvious, for example, from even a casual reflection on differences in religious, ethical and aesthetic perspectives apparent from behaviour. But if we unearth these philosophies and make them explicit, will we not be in a better position to explain behaviour and, if deemed appropriate, change behaviour? Indeed, philosophers might well act to some extent like psychologists. With their deeper knowledge of philosophical themes, philosophers might be more adept at helping individuals to explain the basic 'philosophies' that drive their behaviour and also advise organisations and governments on likely human behaviour in response to different actions.

It is obvious that we all have a hierarchy of 'givens' that we take for granted: some are very mundane and some more fundamental. We could not proceed with our lives by *incessantly* questioning *all* that we assume. At the mundane level we could not cross a street, drive a car, eat a dinner or even type an essay like this with constant referencing back to what we take as given. However, we also have much deeper 'givens' of a philosophical nature at the other end of the spectrum. These are the concern of these notes.

It was in thinking along these lines that I thought that it would be an interesting exercise for me to try to articulate what *my own* understanding and views were on these topics. This would, without doubt, rediscover wheels turned in the literature many times before or, perhaps, display opinions that have been shown to be dubious by experts in the field. It would also bypass a multitude of arguments and counterarguments that have been proposed and might simply highlight my own limited learning.

---

[5] And, of course, philosophers themselves may have their views shaped by social discussion and interaction.

But that, it seemed to me, did not matter. *The point was to discover more clearly by reflection what my own views were given that I am now in my early 80s,*[6] *with what knowledge I have and with the education and experience that I have enjoyed however restricted that might have been.*

Given this reflection, I might change my philosophies, even at this late stage of my life. I thought that, if I could bring to the surface my own views on these themes, for the most part tacitly held, and articulate them clearly, I may learn more about myself and others might also learn more about me if they choose to do so and believe what I write.

These notes are, therefore, the expression of a particular layman's (my) philosophies and is in no way intended to be an introduction to philosophy for laymen. Moreover, this attempt is really just self-indulgence, but it will be an interesting exercise for me and, possibly, if it is successful, for some of my immediate family and friends. Some time ago I thought of trying to write the history of my life (only for family consumption), but I thought that this will be much more fun for me to do. Moreover, as a retired academic from quite another field, I was used to writing reasonably extensively during my career. I have written nothing for the last thirteen or fourteen years and, perhaps, I felt it was time to try to write something else before it was too late! Yet further, I did not know how much I might have to say beyond a series of disjointed notes, but, having completed my task, I have definitely added considerable clarity to my own thoughts on these issues.[7]

For me to undertake this task, Kenny, op cit, has been essential. In general, I adopted the theme headings close to those he used in his fourth volume as well as Physics that figured in the third volume. I have addressed them in a different order because I wanted to show how I thought knowledge in each theme led to knowledge in themes subsequently addressed. Given my very limited background in philosophical literature, I used Kenny's volumes very closely as my initial guide to what each theme of philosophy is and then

---

[6] I first began developing these notes in my late 70s.

[7] I am aware of Mary Midgley's recent book *What is Philosophy for?*, Bloomsbury 2018, but my text takes quite a different slant on the subject as will be discussed at various points within the text and in drawing my conclusions.

explored my own thoughts about each theme. In that sense this is not really, despite the title of these notes, a layman's view of philosophy. It is, for the most part, a layman's reflection on philosophy as portrayed in Kenny's texts for 2nd and 3rd year undergraduates.[8] Nevertheless, I am one of the possible audiences that Kenny claims for his books – namely one who is simply reading them for enlightenment and entertainment. Because I depended upon these books so much in writing this brief text, it is quite possible that some of my reflections have been considered and dismissed or developed in other philosophical literature, especially since 1975. However, Kenny's books and the few other references that I have used published after 1975 enabled me to achieve my own purpose.

After writing the above, I came across the following quotation in ER House, cited later in the Section on Ethics.

> The first step to understanding of men is the bringing to consciousness of the model or models that dominate and penetrate their thought and action. Like all attempts to make men aware of the categories in which they think, it is a difficult and sometimes painful activity, likely to produce deeply disquieting results.
>
> Isaiah Berlin, *Philosophy, Politics and Society*, 1962, p vii.

In stating the need to bring to consciousness the models (philosophies) that penetrate our thought, it captures exactly what I have tried to do, although I have not found the process painful or disquieting. Indeed, at times, it has been quite stimulating.

My main objective in writing this text was, as explained, to clarify my own views on these different areas of philosophy. Having now done that, I still think that activity was of value and I recommend it to other laymen. However, as I reviewed each area of philosophy and compiled the text my aim expanded somewhat. Having an academic background does, I suppose, give one a critical outlook. Seeing, for example, disputes between

---

[8] Kenny says that he has excluded any philosophical works published after 1975. I have tried to supplement Kenny's work by reading some, but not a great deal, of literature published after 1975.

philosophers and scientists made me want to give my personal evaluation of them. Hence, I take issue with one or two recent philosophical works, but suggest how their views can be linked in with views from science.

I was also uneasy that Kenny did not include science within his last book.[9] That seemed to me to be a major omission and needed to be rectified in order to assess how science is influencing philosophical thought. Before considering philosophy, I therefore commence, in Section 2, with a review of both the science of evolution and current scientific knowledge about the state of the universe. While, if one reads this Section, it may seem that it is taking a long time to reach philosophical issues, it does address is some detail objections by two well-known philosophers, Nagel and Midgley, to the Selfish Gene Theory as an adequate explanation of evolution. This includes whether it is likely that a teleological force is needed, as Nagel suggests, to explain evolution. There is also reference to scientific research relating to Genetic Drift and Recombination and its relevance to explaining evolution.[10] Also, when, later in the text, I address areas of philosophy, I thought it would be interesting not just to explore what each area was, but how it evolved; not just historically as covered very well by Kenny, but to address the question of where did human values like religion, God, ethics, compassion, aesthetics and language, come from in a world which evolved through natural selection. There is therefore quite a lot of reference to evolution throughout the text and the opening section on Darwinism and Neo-Darwinism provides a foundation for much of that.

Then I turn to a discussion of the nature of the universe and the matter within it, including ourselves, where brief consideration is given to the concepts of space and time from both an Einsteinian and Quantum Field Theory perspective. So Section 2, to some extent provides some basic material for later philosophical Sections of this text.

Section 3 argues that the concept of God should be separated from the notion of a religion. The question of whether God exists relies heavily upon the description of the universe in Section 2 and argues how God is

---

[9] Apart from a few references to Darwin.

[10] All terms to be defined in due course.

an evolving concept. In particular, it considers what a valid agnostic stance can be. It is then argued that there is definitely a positive role for religion, despite its shaky theological foundations and it too is an evolving concept.

Section 4 tries to get to grips with one of main current concerns of philosophy; that of the Mind. After a basic consideration of what awareness and consciousness is, a deeper investigation, including both scientific and philosophical works, of consciousness is undertaken. This incorporates the debate as to how far scientific reductionist methodology can ever be expected to explain the workings of the Mind. This then leads into a discussion of the concept of free will and then identity.

Section 5 begins with what 'the person in the street' probably thinks of first when considering ethics. This is mainly a concern to be fair which, at the level of interaction between individuals and groups, seems to be the result of a search for a way to maintain an ordered society which, I believe, also led to the development of religion. The concept of fairness is shown, at rather a different level, also to underpin the very basis of our Western democracy and was achieved more by a historical struggle for rights and not just what was needed for an ordered society. It is also suggested that being fair is quite different from being compassionate and asks where feelings of compassion come from. This Section also includes the question of conflicting moralities and a brief review of ethics literature over time is offered (based extensively on a précis of Kenny). This all leads to the recognition that there is an ethical structure to society and that ethical practice and enforcement is a multilayered. The Section concludes with the enhanced role that religion might play in ethical understanding and observance. There are, hence, evolutionary undertones throughout this Section too.

Section 6 addresses the topics of aesthetics and what various philosophers have said about it. It moves on to compare and contrast aesthetics with more general forms of recreation. It suggests how both aesthetic and recreational practices probably arose.

Having completed Section 6, I realised that by taking the key concepts from the areas of science and philosophy already addressed, I had the basis of defining what a worthwhile life was. This has, of course, been a subject of debate since Aristotle and before. What I wanted to emphasise here was what each of us, *individually*, need to consider in order to judge if our lives are worthwhile. This also led me to extract from my discussion in Sections 2 to 6, five key factors in consider to achieve a worthwhile existence. It also marks a change in direction from what I originally intended in this text to become more 'action orientated' rather than just pondering about my view on different philosophical areas.

Section 7 addresses the area of political philosophy. Given my initial objective in writing this text, I could have simply reviewed the historical development of political philosophy and stated what my views were. However, having developed Section 6, I moved the political philosophy Section to later in the text so that I could then explore the extent to which the five key decision factors identified in Section 6 were relevant in considering Government policy. Accordingly, Section 7 first reviews briefly the history of political philosophy and then spends much longer wondering where the subject might progress in future. To do this, I look at each main Government service bearing in mind the five key factors mentioned.

Section 8 is the last philosophical topic to be addressed in this text. It considers whether Wittgenstein's argument that all language is a public language is totally correct when one investigates how language evolved as a means of communication. The use of language for reasons beyond communication is then reviewed leading to the current topical issue of 'fake news'.

The concept of evolution is present in all the Sections of this text. Hence, I have tried to see how various concepts such as competition, collaboration, fairness, compassion, aesthetics, political philosophy and language evolved. In fact, the first half of the text places a heavy emphasis on the notion of evolution. The second half changes the emphasis to look more at practical issues and concludes that there are a number of clear concepts that need to be considered in assessing any human action and, indeed, action by any person or organisation in authority. Then, in the section on Conclusions, I summarise my review of different areas of philosophy and what that has meant for my own thinking, right or wrong. Given the emphasis throughout on evolution, this review led me to consider the nature of social change. Finally, I state briefly what the future role of philosophy might encompass.

At the outset, when I first read Kenny's volumes, I would not have dared to make such claims. I hope that they do have some substance.

In my earlier drafts I also commenced this text with Sections on Logic and Ontology and Epistemology. These are, obviously, basic considerations for any text which aims to discuss the nature of reality. However, these are now included as Appendices at the end of the text. As my text and argument developed, it became very clear, despite Kenny, that a discussion of science was now vital when considering different fields of philosophy. It would have diverted attention from this not to commence with a Section on science. Hence, that is what I have done. The material now in Appendices would have obscured this main message. Readers will find only some limited discussion of philosophy in this Section 2 on science, but be assured that the material there does underpin a number of arguments in the remainder of the text.

2.

Science – Some Biology and Physics

In the introduction to his fourth volume[11] Kenny says that he has dropped Physics (which used to be referred to as 'natural philosophy') from consideration as a separate topic in his book on modern philosophy. He says this is because, since Newton, physics has become 'a fully mature science independent of philosophical underpinning.' Kenny is, for the most part correct,[12] but, in my view, a section on physics and also biology, to include the methods of scientific enquiry, was vital for these notes. Philosophy is no longer independent from some scientific underpinning. In fact, I think it was a major omission by Kenny to exclude a consideration of science. The development of science has achieved so much in the last 200 years that it must now be one, but not the only, bedrock of philosophical thinking. While I am neither a trained scientist nor philosopher, in writing this text, especially the first half of it, it became obvious to me that developments in physics and biology will increasingly affect how we see the world and hence must influence philosophical thinking. In particular, it cannot be avoided in addressing, for example, the topics of God, Consciousness and Political Philosophy and the stimulation of Innovation. All this will be addressed later in this text.

So what do I, a non-scientist, think that the physical sciences are and why are they separate from philosophy? The scientific process of enquiry aims to discover the truth about how nature works. It uses a Realist approach as

---

[11] Kenny, op cit, vol 4.

[12] There is still scope for interaction between scientists and philosophers to develop ideas in some areas such as a consciousness as discussed later in this text. Kenny is also obviously aware how advances in physics can influence philosophy, but he states that this can only be pursued by those with more knowledge of modern science than can be presumed in the readership of his introductory history of philosophy, Vol 3, p 180. I beg to differ. One need have only an outline understanding of developments in science since the 19th century to be able to suggest some impact it has had on philosophical concepts.

defined in Appendix 3. It develops theories and then seeks factual evidence to support or refute those theories. The obvious question arises: where do these theories come from? Most probably they arise from men thinking about their observations, but clearly they can arise out of thought experiments not based upon observation at all.[13] This emphasises that theories are developed by human thought. That may well proceed incrementally in thinking about the implications of past discoveries or observations and, hence, provide some sequence to development of our knowledge, but there can also be 'logical leaps' which may or may not lead to transformations and redirections of our search for knowledge. In addition, the social context in which the scientist operates may influence what it is socially acceptable to theorise about and what is not.[14] Developments in *theories* about physical science may, therefore, not be only the product of the scientific process itself. Nevertheless, however the theories are derived, they must be tested against factual data and, normally, these tests need to be replicated, for the whole process to be labelled as the scientific method.

This also implies that the reliability of results of such a process depends upon the reliability of the measurements used to establish the facts. Moreover, theories can never be proven to apply in all possible situations. There is always the possibility that a situation will be discovered where the theory does not hold, but most of the knowledge we hold as firm in physical science will have been shown to exist in many tests or situations. Even then scientists may only be able to show that the theory holds most of the time without being able to explain fully when it may not. Physical science therefore takes reality as a given – there is a physical world operating out there which is quite separate from our human individuality and it can be tested.

I focus on two main areas of science: first, the science of evolution and, second, the science of the nature of the universe. I am very aware that I am not a scientist and so my understandings of these areas may be misguided

---

[13] Einstein riding on a beam of light comes to mind as one of the most far-reaching thought experiments we have known.

[14] The situation that Galileo faced comes to mind here.

or simplistic. However, it seems very important to consider these topics in particular and how they must influence thinking about different areas of philosophy. As the object of writing this text is to unearth *my own* layman views on areas of philosophy, it is *my understanding* of these areas of science that must underpin my views. For what it is worth, this text is a layman's view.

The Theory of Evolution of the Species: Two Philosophers' Critiques Reviewed

The current dominant scientific view on how Man arrived at his present state is based on an updated version of Darwinian Theory of Evolution. According to Darwin, organisms (like you and me, all living beings and our ancestors) have different traits and, in the competition for resources needed for survival, only those whose traits were best suited to their environments survived.[15] This was called the process of natural selection and explained how species developed and new ones were formed. Since Darwin, scientists have gained an understanding of genetics and Neo-Darwinism superimposes on the idea of natural selection the mutation of genes as the basic mechanism by which organisms adapt. More recently, Dawkins[16] presented a refined version of this model of evolution. My truncated understanding of his theory is as follows.

Dawkins begins his book by suggesting how life began by some molecules sticking together and then starting to replicate leading to life in its earliest form. These replicators (genes), he surmised, became incorporated into organisms which merely act as vehicles for ensuring the ongoing life of the genes. Each organism has a collection of genes (genomes) which give rise to the attributes (traits, phenotypes) which determine how it behaves and survives to reproduce and thereby enable the continuity of genes.[17] Note

---

[15] AR Wallace quite separately proposed the same theory. See R Dawkins, *Science in the Soul*, Random House, 2017, pp 108–118.

[16] R Dawkins, *The Selfish Gene*, Oxford University Press, 1976. There is, of course, a massive literature relating to Darwinism, but only a brief outline is needed here.

[17] Genotypes are the collection of genes in an organism. Phenotypes describe the features

that it is the continuity of the *genes* that drives evolution. Organisms carry the gene in their chromosomes[18] and then pass it on from one generation to the next. In replication of the genes some random 'mistakes' occur (genetic mutation) leading to changes in the genes which produce changes in the genotype, which leads to the organism having different attributes. Hence, physical evolution of the organism occurs. If the change in the organism makes it better suited for reproduction in its environment, its progeny will survive at the expense of those organisms less suited and will serve as a better vehicle for the ongoing existence of the genes which are transferred from generation to generation as each of its transporter organisms dies. More precisely, it is the genotypes that provide the fittest organisms for survival and the mutated gene that gets attached to the better mix of other genes and so stands a better chance of longer survival itself. Even so, like the organism, the genotype will be short-lived compared to the gene. It is the latter which, as Dawkins says, is the unit that survives through many successive bodies. So it is the random mutation of genes coupled with ongoing modification of the genotypes that brings about the change in physical traits of organisms as a by-product of the process of furthering the life of genes. Likewise, it is the quality of the gene pool which determines the long-run viability and evolution of the species. Over the long run this can lead to a species dividing into more than one species. It is important to note, however, that, according to this theory, there is no purpose behind this physical evolution. It just happens.

There is a further way in which one can think about what Man is from an internal perspective. Developments in biology and medical science have shown how Man, and indeed all living matter, evolved from one initial cell. From this early time, viruses also existed. These viruses, being unable to reproduce themselves unaided, invaded cells to make use of the cell's

---

(size, colour etc.) of an organism. The genotype is the cause and the phenotype is the effect. Genotypes specify what is particular about the DNA of an organism and is often used to discuss a subgroup of genes. Genomes always refer to the sum of all the organism's genes. A gene pool is something different yet again. A gene pool refers to the collection of genes in the whole population under consideration.

[18] A chromosome is a whole strand of DNA while genes are part of it.

material to do so. Man now consists of thousands of cells and they are still in continual battle with viruses which try to destroy cells. When viruses get the upper hand, Man suffers disease as very evident from the recent coronavirus outbreak. Only in recent decades, so I understand, has Man managed to gain a deeper understanding of the detailed processes within cells by which viruses do this and how cells try to defend themselves. Research is still ongoing in this field. Recognition of this has significance for understanding what Man is because, I am told, it is the process of battle between a virus and a cell that contributes towards genetic mutations mentioned above which, in turn, fuel evolution.[19]

Two well-known philosophers have relatively recently been very critical of Dawkins' theory. Thomas Nagel argued strongly that Darwinism and the Dawkins' Selfish Gene Theory could not possibly account for all the diversity of life that exists in the world. He felt so strongly that he chose a provocative subtitle for his book.[20] He argued that there had been insufficient geological time for all the necessary mutations to take place, although his view, at least as expressed in his book, seems to be based on little more than a general

---

[19] As an aside, clearly, Man and all other life forms have evolved from that initial cell going through many different stages of development. Individually, or as a species, we tend to see Man as a fairly stable phenomenon. Yet why should we suppose that evolution is over? Taking a very long-term view over much of the history of the Earth, the current understanding of Man may be seen as just a transitional stage in a long competitive game.

[20] T Nagel, *Mind and Cosmos – why the Materialist Neo-Darwinian Conception of Nature is almost certainly false*, Oxford University Press, 2012. He has not been the only author to commence a book in such dramatic fashion. AN Wilson, in his recent book, *Charles Darwin, Victorian Mythmaker*, Harper Collins, 2017, begins his Prelude with the words, capitalised, 'DARWIN WAS WRONG'. Wilson tried to establish his case by a more detailed analysis of Darwin's theory than Nagel's much more vague comments. However, Wilson has been subject to very severe criticism by several scientists who have reviewed his book (Jones, [*Sunday Times*, 10.9.2017], Woolfson [*Evening Standard*, 24.8.2017], van Wyhe [New Scientist, 21.8.2017] and Rutherford [*Review for Amazon*, 11.9.2017]. They all said that Wilson's explanation of Darwinian Theory leaves much to be desired. (Although he presents a very interesting description of Darwin's life.) This suggests that non-experts entering this field, as both Wilson and I are, should beware and recognise their own limitations. If necessary, I fall back on the defence that my initial intention was to establish clearly what I thought and how that influences my layman's view on philosophy even if it is shown that these thoughts are in need of modification.

belief. At the end of his Introduction he says:

> ... with regard to evolution, the process of natural selection cannot account for the actual history without an adequate supply of viable mutations, and, I believe it remains an open question whether this could have been provided in geological time merely as a result of chemical accident, without the operation of some other factors determining and restricting the forms of genetic variation.

While Nagel was careful to say that it is still 'an open question', he makes it pretty clear throughout the rest of his book that he is quite sceptical of 'speculative Darwinian explanations of practically everything' and the almost universal reliance of the advancement of our knowledge upon reductionist materialistic (physicalist) principles. He proposes that universal teleological laws may exist, as well as physical laws,[21] with the former required as additional inputs for understanding the world we live in. In other words, evolution does not just happen, there is some directional purpose behind it. He also says that he does not know what such a teleological force is.[22] He

---

[21] In philosophy, teleology means events and objects have a purpose and that there is some sense of direction or convergence in events where there some paths are far more likely to be adopted than others. Nagel does not believe in a totally physicalist world (closely associated with materialism), but that natural teleological laws probably exist as well as physical laws to explain life and consciousness. Most philosophers reject this and do believe in physicalism. See D Bourget and D Chalmers, 'What do most philosophers believe?', *Philosophical Sciences*, 170, 465–500, 2013. No doubt most scientists are also physicalists. The question of consciousness will be addressed later in Section 4. For the moment it is sufficient to note that what Nagel seems to be saying with regard to evolution is simply that this teleological law implies that mutation of the genes is not random, but driven by an organising force which accelerates evolution. If this is correct, it is important because he still accepts that gene mutation is the basis for evolution; it is just the generation of the mutation which is different. The notion of teleology must be distinguished quite clearly from the concept of intention as generally understood. Teleology is understood as a basic law of the universe, not an individual animal or human intention. Similarly, an individual having an intention is not the same in philosophy as 'intentionality' which states that an individual's mental states have intentionality as they have mental representations of things, real or unreal, i.e. they have contents. I will refer to intentions and how they have had a significant role to play in evolution and, when I do so, I mean individual intentions as understood in everyday language.

[22] Nagel is, though, in agreement with Dawkins that the teleological factor is not God.

just wants to raise the problem.

Midgley,[23] writing quite separately from Nagel, also says, in commenting on Dawkins' book:

> … he suggested in the preface to The Selfish Gene that his readers should enjoy the book simply as an exciting story. He was trying to eat the fiction-cake and also have it – to produce extra enjoyment without admitting that the book, which indeed contains a great deal of fantasy, might not actually all be literally true.[24]

She then says, like Nagel, that it is clear that some other factors influenced evolution and it could not have all been due to *random genetic mutation* alone in the geological time that has been available. She says that even Darwin said so.[25] Arguing similarly to Nagel, she says 'evolution needs an indicator of direction.'

There are four entangled issues in these two philosophers' arguments that need to be unravelled and addressed separately in order to assess the validity of their claims.

1. Has there been sufficient geological time for the necessary quantity of gene mutations to have taken place to produce the variety of species we see today?

2. Second, as raised more precisely by Nagel, has *all* gene mutation giving rise to evolution been random?

3. Third, more generally, is the complete process of evolution described by the Selfish Gene Theory a totally random one and has some directional force been involved?

4. Fourth, is there a need to identify a teleological force to help explain evolution.

---

[23] M Midgley, *What is philosophy for?*, Bloomsbury Academic, 2018.

[24] Midgley just refers to the first few words of Dawkins' Preface. Later she also criticises Crick quite strongly when only referring to the opening words on his book on Consciousness to which attention will be paid later in this text.

[25] Midgley, op cit p 108.

My answers are 'Yes' to the first and second questions, but in addressing them one must not confuse gene mutation with changes in genomes which determine organisms' traits which, as argued below, can be brought about without gene mutation. Regarding the third issue, the Selfish Gene Theory does not propose a completely random process and so it cannot be refuted on the basis that it is totally random. Also if one's objective is to explain the current diversity of life on Earth, rather than just support or refute the Selfish Gene Theory, there are plenty of examples of intentions and other effects which have contributed to evolution. Fourth, there is no reason to suppose that a teleological force is at work as Nagel suggests.

Question 1. Has the world existed for long enough for the necessary number of mutations that could lead to the present diversity of life? Answer 'Yes'.

The argument on the question of the adequacy of geological time for the Selfish Gene Theory to determine all evolution has taken place for many years. Lord Kelvin argued, in the late 19th century, that the Earth was 20 million years old, it was questioned whether this had been a long enough time for random genetic variation to have brought about the evolution that has occurred. However, Rutherford showed in 1904 that this estimate had to be increased by a considerable magnitude to 4.5 billion years and, from the viewpoint of whether there had been sufficient time for evolution by genetic mutation, it seemed that Darwin's argument was rescued. Moreover, as discussed below, developments in biology suggest that there is good scientific reason to question whether *all* biological evolution could have been due to random gene mutation and so the time needed would not have been so long as if evolution depended solely on random genetic mutation.

Question 2. Has all mutation of genes been random? Answer 'Yes', but all variation in genotypes has not been due to gene mutation.

To consider this question it is useful to address the research of Wagner,[26] but he suggests a digression is needed first to understand the notion of a

---

[26] A Wagner, *Life Finds a Way*, One World, 2019.

24

'fitness landscape' introduced by Wright[27] in the 1930s to explain his work on animal breeding. This landscape can be envisaged as a multidimensional graph with 'horizontal' axes showing the degree of traits possessed by organisms and the vertical axis showing the degree of fitness. If the organism had only three traits, one can think of this as three-dimensional plotting of a mountain, with those who, through evolution, have the most suitable combination of traits reaching the summit. If there were just one mountain peak of suitable fitness, this would be attainable, over a suitable expanse of time, through just gene mutation and natural selection. Of course, organisms usually have many more than three different traits. The real fitness landscape in fact has thousands of dimensions. One might think in terms of different breeds of sheep. Some better for providing wool; some better for meat and so on. Wright recognised this and suggested that the fitness landscape was not in the form of a single dominant mountain, but in the form of a mountain range with various peaks at different heights and valleys and ridges between them. Different collections of traits would be associated with the ability to attain some peaks but not others, unless there were a change in the population genomes and traits.[28] Another possibility might be that the environment changes and then traits that previously could only achieve one level of fitness might be able to progress further.

With a multiple peak fitness range, if evolution could only take place by gene mutation and natural selection, an organism placed at the foot of one particular mountain because of its existing traits would only be able to travel up that specific mountain. Any small change in gene pool would provide the basis for a small improvement or not, and, if not, it would be rejected. If an improvement were offered, the being would go a little higher towards the peak which might be just a local maximum, not necessarily the top of the whole range. To achieve a transfer to the slope going up to the overall

---

[27] S Wright, The roles of mutation, inbreeding, crossbreeding and selection in evolution, *Proceedings of the Sixth International Congress of Genetics in Ithaca*, New York, 1, 356, 1932. (Not seen by the author, but discussed based on content in Wagner, *Life Finds a Way*, op cit).

[28] We see this around us in human life. There is not one absolute norm of fitness. People have varying levels of fitness for different tasks which enable them to exist and reproduce.

maximum, it is necessary either to introduce an alternative mechanism which changes the population gene pool or to see the whole environment change in favour of a previously non-optimal set of traits. Wagner fully accepts that genetic mutation with natural selection is the bedrock of evolution, but, he says, there are two other processes on top of the Selfish Gene idea that can lead to physical change in organisms and species. Wagner[29] introduces the notion of Genetic Drift (historically called the Sewall Wright Effect) as the first of his two alternative mechanisms.

Genetic Drift views populations as not just a collection of organisms, but as a collection of genes and the traits to which they are linked. Genes are passed on from one generation to the next by combining the genes from each parent. If the population consisted of just two people, who then had a girl and a boy, who bred and then had another girl and a boy and this process continued over time, the 'population' traits would become more concentrated with some going extinct and the process continuing until all had the same traits. Therein lay the danger of inbreeding. If one of the traits at the outset was bad, i.e. susceptible to disease, the whole population could contract it. With a much reduced gene pool the population would have a different set of traits and be headed for a different route in evolution. So Genetic Drift can even cause a whole population to become extinct without any mutation of genes.

The larger the population, the more generations it takes for Genetic Drift to result in all members of that population carrying the same trait. In very large populations the likelihood of that happening is so very small that it can be ignored. However, Genetic Drift is still at work changing the population gene pool without any help from gene mutation. Moreover, unlike progress through genetic mutation and natural selection, which is unidirectional, Genetic Drift can enable improvement up the fitness landscape *or a slide down it*. By sliding down, it offers the possibility of forming a different structure of the population gene pool and, hence, the chance of moving to a different mountain or even creating a new species. *Wagner says that Genetic Drift is at least as important in evolution as gene mutation.*

---

[29] A Wagner, *Life Finds a Way*, op cit.

Wagner also describes a second alternative mechanism to gene mutation called Recombination. Recombination is different from Genetic Drift and, whereas drift in very large populations will be marginal, Recombination can cause much larger leaps in the change process. We have 23 chromosomes that contain our genes. Each chromosome comes in a pair giving us two copies of each gene. When fertilising female egg cells with male sperm, cell division occurs whereby each member of a chromosome pair exchanges DNA text with their partner. This is called Recombination – each chromosome becomes a mosaic of its previous DNA and that of its partner in the pair and just one from this pair gets incorporated into each sperm or egg cell. Then when sex occurs, a fertilised egg is produced by a Recombination of the 23 rearranged chromosomes from each of the father and mother which gives rise to a new genome for the offspring and, hence, a new phenotype. *The Recombination process also has nothing to do with gene mutation, but it operates on the genes available at the time of Recombination which are obviously the result of past mutations and occasionally new ones. Random genetic mutation is the basic foundation of evolution. It is just not a total explanation.* It is the Recombination of genes from the father and mother by forming new genomes that offers the prospect of different traits. The more different are the DNA of the father and mother, a greater leap in genome is possible. The greatest change is where members of different species mate.[30] Wagner says this can be disastrous and lead to dead ends in evolution (e.g. in mules, lion-tiger hybrids, zebra-horse hybrids),[31] but it can also lead to new species instantly.[32]

So Recombination can be working away bringing about the evolution of organisms even if there has not been much random mutation. Hence, the development of all the current diversity of life on Earth may not have to

---

[30] I am aware that a definition of species implies different species could not mate with each other. In general they don't.

[31] Hybridisation can be very successful with plants and some animals.

[32] Wagner also explains how bacteria, not reproducing sexually as we do, have a process of horizontal gene transfer which achieves the same end. Recombination is, hence, near universal in nature.

await all random genetic mutations, giving more credibility to the view that geological time has been sufficient to bring about this diversity. It might be added that Dawkins is quite aware of Recombination; he has a number of different references to Recombination throughout his *Ancestor's Tale*.[33]

Of course, breeding and cross-breeding of plants and animals (a form of Recombination) has been undertaken for centuries in order to produce better stock. The ability to do this brought about the developments in population genetics.

> Darwin himself already reminded us in the *Origin of the Species* of how much diversity human breeders have created in some species.[34]

It would seem, however, that this can only bring about changes in the mix of different organisms that comprise a species. It cannot change genes; that can only be achieved by mutation. It can, however, change mixtures of genes (genotypes), phenotypes and gene pools via the battle for survival. Of course, this has only occurred since Man with a brain has evolved and this was very late in geological time.

The discussion on this question leads me to hypothesise that more of microevolution, that is the changes in the nature of organisms within a species, is probably mainly due to Recombination whereby the probability distribution of outcomes can be fairly reliably determined. This is operating all the time and bringing about changes in the shorter term, but is evolution nonetheless. In contrast the Selfish Gene Theory, perhaps, accounts for more long-term macroevolution, that is changes to create new species through several random mutations of genes over longer spans of time with the outcomes far less predictable. Although, it still seems possible that a single mutation of gene or Recombination could lead to a new species. This is purely my own speculation, I have no evidence for it.

---

[33] R Dawkins, *The Ancestor's Tale*, Weidenfeld & Nicolson, 2004 updated 2016. He also discusses both *random* Genetic Drift and Recombination in R Dawkins, *Science in the Soul*, Random House, 2017, but there I get the impression that his main objective is to emphasise that the adaptive complexity of evolution cannot take place without a non-random selection process.

[34] Wagner, *Life Finds a Way*, op cit, p 16.

Question 3. Is the whole process proposed by the Selfish Gene Theory (not just genetic mutation) a random one or have there been directional influences on evolution? Answer. It is not random.

Neo-Darwinian Theory and Selfish Gene Theory are *not* completely random processes. It is invalid, therefore, to dismiss these theories as if they were. They specify two parts to the evolution process. There is the *random* mutation of genes and the *non-random* natural selection of the fittest for survival. Natural selection is directed in the sense that it leads to adaptive improvement, although it is not, of course, directive if that term is taken to mean guided by intelligent action.[35] One can, however, refer to examples of how intelligent influences have influenced evolution, even if this is not prescribed in the Selfish Gene Theory.

One example has been mentioned already: that of breeding. That clearly involves human intention to achieve microevolution. Closely related to breeding is genetic editing. This has largely been at the level of excluding or replacing genes and not modifying the gene per se. I believe that there has been some exception to this where damaged genes have been repaired, but I have no idea how widespread this activity has been undertaken. Nevertheless, if such repaired genes are passed on between generations, that would be like a mutation, but it would not have been randomly mutated. In any case, such activity is only very recent in the vast history of time and, hence, not very relevant in explaining the current diversity of life on Earth. It does, however, demonstrate how human intention is becoming a more significant factor in determining what organisms survive.

Dawkins[36] also discusses the possible origin of agriculture arising from hunter-gatherers husbanding herds to protect them against rival hunters or other enemies and even starting to feed them. This could have led to corralling and housing them. The animals then became more domesticated and, hence, our ancestors had inadvertently changed the selection pressures on these animals. Within the gene pools of animals it was no longer vital to

---

[35] R Dawkins, *Science in the Soul*, op cit, p 227.

[36] The *Ancestor's Tale* once more.

have fleetness of foot or other survival skills and different animals evolved. A similar process took place in the evolution of grey wolves into all our current breeds of dogs. Such developments resulted from the emergence of more animals with particular genome patterns and gene pool change, but not through mutation of genes, but through cultural change in the way Man lived. Clearly, intention was involved here.

Examples of how changes in the mix of genotypes in the species occur also come from Dawkins himself. Dawkins[37] states, a version of ape that was Man's ancestor developed the ability to stand on two legs, rather than all fours and this could have been due to the intent to reach sources of food on higher branches, the need to wade cross rivers or swamps or even preferences of the opposite sex. Sexual preference was also offered as an explanation for those with larger brain size being preferred for sexual reproduction. Those with ability to stand on two legs or possessing larger brain size, therefore passed on their genes to increase the number of organisms with upright standing or large brains. The same phenomenon is said to have occurred with the peacock's tail. Males with most attractive tails were preferred by females, so the number of long tail peacocks increased. So we may conclude that the intention of the organism had a key part to play in the evolution of different mixes of organisms within a species. It is very important to recognise, once more, exactly what this implies with regard to random gene mutation. The change in the practice of some apes to stand on two legs rather than four legs (and the other changes mentioned above) was not the result of genetic mutation. Certainly, the genes enabled members of the species to do this, but the change in practice did not take place until the need to do so arose. Then the change was intent driven.

It is also clear that Man has been a chief factor in the extinction of some species that he hunted for food. A notable example is the extinction of the woolly mammoth. The traits of the mammoth were not such that it could compete with those of Man and so it did not survive, but Man had to think out and have clear intention of how to use his own traits to capture the

---

[37] R Dawkins, *The Ancestor's Tale*, op cit, pp 222–230.

mammoth.[38]

A close association with this argument applies in the case of all more advanced species, that is those with brains. A conscious choice *is* made in order to survive. Whatever genes a being has, it must take a decision in order to survive. Mammals hunt or otherwise search for food and, if they happen to be the prey for other mammals, they are pretty intent on avoiding being caught. The extent to which they manage to eat or escape danger is very much the result of *both* genetic ability and the *will to survive*, with the latter also an integral part of the pattern of evolution. Variations in the strength of will to survive may also be part of the organism's genetic heritage, but there has to be *intent* on the part of members of different species to make use of their genetic heritage – they are not automatons.

A recent TV programme also showed how the ability of animals to learn to build dams, construct homes/nests, etc., have all contributed to their ability to survive. Of course, they could not do this without the appropriate genetic inheritance, but the more successful at doing this survived to form part of the current diversity of life. Similarly, many groups of animals collaborate to achieve their ends, sometimes across species. Directional intent is involved.

Man has improved the quality and enlarged his sources of food through agriculture. He has also improved his living conditions. This has led to a clear increased body size and better health. This did not, perhaps, cause a mutation of the gene, but the improved food is also available to the offspring so that they too may develop increased body size. In addition, those with genes more able to take advantage of more and better food to create increased size could, once more, have passed on their genes to create more large people via sexual activity.

On the other hand, through Nutrigenomics, we also know that certain foods can influence the way genes operate. For example, diet can influence weight, blood pressure, cholesterol and cancer growth. Again, as I understand it, food does not alter the genes, but, observance of different diets can

---

[38] The introduction of an organism's intention here, remember, is not the same as introducing a universal teleological force.

switch some genes on or off and that would be reflected to some extent in different bodily attributes. So changing diets over time can generate physical evolution within a species if not macroevolution.

Furthermore, for some years now scientists have been able to undertake genome editing (that is replacing or removing genes in the DNA) which will also change then phenotype. This has long been undertaken regarding plants and, more recently, in tackling human disease. This actually does change the set of genes that would otherwise be passed to the next generation. In treating human disease, this may mean that offspring do not get defective genes possessed by the parent. In much genome editing in plants, new stronger varieties evolve encouraged by human intervention.

Intention is also involved where developments in medical science have led to Man living longer and being able to resist some diseases and viruses due to the development of vaccines. Generally, I understand, vaccines cannot cause mutation of genes,[39] but some can cut out certain genes from the DNA. Then the genotype of offspring will be altered and, in turn, their phenotypes. Certainly, Man has recently undertaken genome editing, but this is just the modification of the genome, rather than change in the gene itself. However, on fewer occasions, scientists have worked on repairing damaged or mutated genes. This would not invalidate the Selfish Gene Theory except that such changes in the gene would not be random. Admittedly, these influences could only be applicable to the latest stages of the very long history of evolution. Such work has been carried out for only a speck in the elapse of time for life on Earth, but it could make a big difference to physical evolution in future.

Also, discussion in the Appendix to Section 4 suggests that the way Men learned to live together *may* have increased the physical size of their brains.[40] If so, there was clear purpose behind the development.

---

[39] Although they can, if successful, render virus mutations inoperative.

[40] Or, a more Darwinian approach would say that those with larger brains may have been better able to operate in social groups and hence survive. On the other hand, later arguments in this text relating to the Mind suggest that the brain can be influenced by experience. Perhaps there was a mixture of both influences.

Leaving the part played by intentions aside, if one wants a full explanation of how we have the current diversity of life on Earth, it is relevant to include here how natural events have influenced evolution, sometimes bringing about very large leaps in development. Dawkins[41] states how the largest ever mass extinction of species occurred a quarter of a million years ago when 95 per cent of all species went extinct. Much later, about 65 million years ago, the Age of the Dinosaurs was ended, leading to the Age of the Mammals. It is not known exactly what caused these events, but a strike by asteroid, meteor or comet may have been the cause and or else massive volcanic activity. Following the extinction of the dinosaurs,[42] small shrew-like creatures had survived the catastrophe which killed off the dinosaurs and expanded into the ecological space made available. So major natural events, which change the environment, can enable certain types of organisms to develop and influence the world's mix of species. It can wipe out some species and accelerate growth in the population of others. Each creature's phenotype will help to determine which creatures survive and those phenotypes will have been acquired via earlier genetic mutation, but, if the major catastrophe had not occurred we would have a different mix of species on Earth now – and it may well have not included us! When such major events occur, evolution does not have to await the appropriate mutation of genes to cause adaptation. Natural selection immediately gets to work on the genetic material remaining after the major event.

Another major environmental event was the Ice Age (or Ice Ages). This suddenly restricted habitable living space and sources of food for some types of life and may, therefore, have been a determinant of the survival of different species. Some species were able to adjust and relocate to other parts of the world and survive, others were not. Also, perhaps those that did relocate met resistance from species already there and this resulted in conflict and, possibly, decimation of some species and growth of others. It is said that competition between humans and Neanderthals may be an example of this. The extinction of the Neanderthals may have been due to the inferiority

---

[41] R Dawkins, *The Ancestor's Tale*, Weidenfeld & Nicolson, pp 144–145.

[42] Strictly most dinosaurs because some survived and mutated into birds.

of their traits compared to those of Homo Sapiens and the success of the latter in exercising control over reduced food and space. If this was so, a species shift was caused by both an initial triggering by the natural event followed by intentions of the two forms of organism being in competition. The Neanderthals may have had different phenotypes from Homo Species due to genetic mutations in their different histories, but their demise was caused by the effect of the Ice Age and the intentions of Neanderthals and Homo Sapiens in response to it. Without them, the Neanderthal species would not have been wiped out.

Moreover, the natural event need not have been as dramatic as meteors striking Earth or Ice Ages. There are many instances of species dying out as the environment changed and this is still occurring. This must alter the food chain for some creatures and thereby affect population size. Some species may have been killed off by other species showing that natural selection had given them a better ability to survive, but there would have been clear intention to survive as well. This would imply, perhaps, that organisms had variations in the determination to survive in the their genomes they inherited and it would be quite consistent with Neo-Darwinism for more determined organisms to remove others from existence, but, in a sense, there was intention.

Wagner,[43] writing recently, gives another example of evolution due to events without reliance on mutation of genes. His example draws upon work involving breeding by Mendel in the mid-1800s, but especially by Sewall Wright in the 1930s,[44] Wagner explains how it is important in

---

[43] A Wagner, *Arrival of the Fittest*, Oneworld, 2014.

[44] AN Wilson, op cit, pp 258–259, in his critique of Darwinism, refers to the hostile 19th century review of Darwinism by S Wilberforce for *The Quarterly Review* which was based on two main points. First that Darwin's analogy between breeding and natural selection was totally misplaced because breeding does not create new species but merely modification of species. That, he said, was not evolution because if a species is returned to the wild, it will revert to its initial state. Second, Darwin had simply dismissed Lyell's statement that geological evidence provided no evidence of transitional forms of one species forming into another and argued that that merely indicated there was lack of evidence of such transition. Wilson then says that, to his knowledge, no one has satisfactorily answered those criticisms. Taking the second first, there have been according to Rutherford (reviewer of Wilson's book)

understanding evolution to see how whole species or populations change over time. Wagner gives an example of the white-bodied peppered moth. That moth has wings flecked with black spots and this gives it camouflage when on the bark of a tree and makes it difficult to be spotted by hungry birds. Some of the species have a genetic mutation that produces very dark winged moths and these are, therefore, more at risk of being spotted by birds. However, during the Industrial Revolution many trees turned black and dark moths were then concealed on tree bark, but the white spattered variety became 'easy meat'. As Wagner says, the proportion of black moths changed from 2 per cent in 1848 to 95 per cent in 1895. This is another case where genetic mutation had no part to play in the evolution, it was a change in the environment, brought about this time by Man. It is important to note that this is not an example of Lamarckism whereby it was thought that organisms bodily adapt to their environment. The environment changed enabling those moths which already had more suitable phenotypes could thrive.

One can, therefore, conclude on Question 3 that the Darwinian process is not totally random. The Selfish Gene Theory should not be criticised because it is totally random, because it is not. There have been directional guides of non-intelligent and intelligent form with the latter becoming gradually more and more influential after organisms gained brains. Indeed, becoming much more influential in the most recent stage of evolution.

Question 4. Is there a need for a teleological force as an explanation? Answer. 'No'.

The answers to Questions 1 to 3 really answer Question 4 as well. It has been argued that the variety of species that exists now has arisen through a

---

millions (perhaps slight exaggeration) of transitional fossils and, regarding the first criticism, Wilberforce was effectively arguing that microevolution does not count. Dawkins (*Science in the Soul*, op cit, p 25) says that most biologists now think that macroevolution is nothing more than microevolution stretched out over a very long time span. I also wonder what evidence Wilson has, or Wilberforce had, that a spaniel or corgi would become a wolf when returned to the wild. They are more likely to fail to survive. I think we can take it that breeding is part of evolution as natural selection is.

combination of the gene random mutations, Genetic Drift, Recombination, directional adaptive improvements (natural selection), intelligent intentions and natural events. This seems to be enough to explain the current pattern of life on Earth without resorting to teleological forces.

So one can immediately say that Nagel and Midgley are correct in saying that random genetic mutation alone cannot explain evolution. However, Nagel was probably incorrect to imply that there was some directional force behind the gene mutation itself. In the case of Genetic Drift and Recombination, directional force has been in the form of sexual activity and they have applied to the genomes directly, not the gene mutation. Many natural events have also change the pattern of life on Earth leading to changes in the environment and thereby influencing the natural selection process. More broadly, both philosophers were correct to argue that some directional force was needed beyond genetic mutation to explain the current diversity of species , but the above discussion has shown that there are a number of ways in which we already knew that this is true and the force was not teleology.

As a last thought on this matter, mechanical devices are now installed intentionally within human bodies where they will help to overcome deficiencies due to injury or wear and tear. One obvious example is the very widespread replacement of knees and hips or pacemakers. While such replacements to date hardly affect Man's central essence of life, one can countenance more advanced future developments in technology being integrated within living beings to form semi-technological living 'humans'. These developments of Man might see him have implants *within himself* which provide a means of action by those that are otherwise immobilised. Additionally, such developments might enable Man to hold a much wider knowledge store and ready means of accessing it, enhanced computing abilities, enhanced communication ability or enhanced physical power far beyond our present capacities. This is not genetic change, but Man as a species can be seen as a living being still in the process of evolving, both through random processes and by design.

While it is fun to have such flights of fancy, any development of this kind would have significant implications for what Man is and his future role in the world. Moreover, there are signs that these suggestions may become less fanciful. Elon Musk's[45] launch of the firm called *Neuralink* and its intention to install chips within human skulls provides evidence of this, as do similar developments by US firms such as *BrainGate* and *Kernel.* Technological problems and associated regulatory hurdles will mean that progress in this field will be slow. There will, nevertheless, be much for philosophers to debate about the way any progress in this direction is altering what they consider a human being to be and, particularly, its Mind.

Yet further, if by evolution one includes *social* evolution[46] and the way Man organises how he lives, it is obvious that Man has influenced that evolution.[47] So, I conclude again that *the story of evolution is already riddled with purposive intent without involving a teleological force.*

While there seems to be no case for teleological forces or some mysterious universal direction to be necessary for evolution to occur,[48] where animals' purposive behaviour is involved, that intent is driven by a will to survive which seems to be present in all living organisms. It is still very relevant to ask what is the source of this will to survive? This will not probably be known until we learn much more about how life began. Indeed, Nagel does recognise the need for such an advance in knowledge before we can assess the relative importance of currently widely accepted evolution theory. So I should place a caveat upon my rejection of a teleological force. Perhaps there is a teleological force inherent in all organisms which does not play a part in the operation of the Selfish Gene Theory, but does drive the more basic *intention to survive.* I think it unlikely and I cannot conceive of any form it might take, but there is still a lot we do not know.

There is one very clear truth emerging from the arguments above. The discussion of evolution above is based on the need to compete to survive

---

[45] Of Tesla and SpaceX fame.

[46] And a *Theory of Everything* should include this too.

[47] Albeit that this is very late in the chain of evolution.

[48] In challenging reliance on the Selfish Gene Model, Nagel points out, in a footnote, that some evolutionary biologists have suggested that the randomness on genetic variation that is possible may be subject to limits. However, this not really relevant to Nagel's argument for a teleological element in evolution.

– either to compete against other living creatures or against conditions thrown up by nature. Irrespective of the acceptability of the Selfish Gene Theory, organisms compete to survive. Man is no exception. Indeed, he competes at various different levels: in his cells, as an organism and in groups, species and nations. Competition is, therefore, pervasive to all life. Moreover, it does not make sense to discuss competition unless one considers competition between what entities, in other words between what identities.[49] One competes to maintain an identity at the expense of another identity or in a changed environment. Recognition of this must be fundamental in considering subsequent sections of this text, especially Ethics and Political Philosophy.

Again, however, considerable care is needed to consider what this pervasiveness of competition to life means. Wilson[50] ends his book by saying that Darwin and Neo-Darwinian Theory suggests two erroneous ideas,[51] the second of which concerns us here:

> The second idea, that nature is everlastingly at war, and that evolutionary progress happens by conflict, is almost the reverse of the truth.[52]

Wilson also refers to Spikins[53] who says that:

> evolution, both biologically and socially, has been about groups of people (collaborating) not all of them strong and powerful.

---

[49] The nature of human identity is discussed later in Section 4 of this text.

[50] AN Wilson, op cit.

[51] The first so-called erroneous idea is that all evolution is gradual and that nature never leaps and that if Darwin were correct there would be thousands of transitional fossils. Well, as stated earlier, according to the review of one of his critics (Dr Adam Rutherford) there are many such fossils. Also Rutherford states that Darwin's concept of gradualism only argues that a single organism cannot immediately give birth to a different species and that Darwin's contribution was that, through natural selection, different species can emerge over time. The essence of Darwin's Theory was about this and not the speed of change.

[52] AN Wilson, op cit, p 367.

[53] P Spikins, *How compassion made us human: the evolutionary origins of tenderness, trust and morality*, Pen and Sword Books, 2015.

There is also the suggestion in Spikins that a female view of the world provides this different perspective.

Of course! Of course! Man (or any other organism) does not have to be in conflict all the time. There seem to be three situations in which we can find ourselves: first, there is not a current threat to us at all and we can happily progress as we are without thinking too much about competition; second, there is competition, but our current way of handling it requires no change and, third, that the threat is so significant that we must adapt to survive. I suggest that we experience all these situations throughout life and these states represent that faced by organisms throughout evolutionary history. That, in no way, undermines the centrality of the need to compete where necessary. The most caring of females will fight tooth and nail to protect her offspring when needed. Competition is the core feature of life. It certainly is often coupled with collaboration, but I will leave that until Section 5.

Following criticism of the Selfish Gene Theory, both Nagel and Midgley move on to argue that the Mind and consciousness cannot be understood via reductionist materialistic methods. They both argue very strongly against the trend they say is becoming established to say everything can be explained by the physical sciences and their deterministic methods. This is quite a jump from their criticism of the Selfish Gene Theory. Even if it were proven that the Selfish Gene Theory were totally false, that has nothing to do with proving that a general approach to materialistic scientific enquiry is reliable or unreliable for exploring the Mind, consciousness, purpose and thought. They are quite separate issues. This will be left aside now to be addressed in Section 4 of this text which focuses on the Mind, but a brief reference is made here to recognise the increasing scientific knowledge about the brain and its operation. Considerable research has been conducted which explains how different parts of the brain relate to different bodily functions. I believe that scientific enquiry may well *eventually* explain the *internal processes* of the brain and show how they are linked to the content of our thought and intentions, although many take the opposite view.

Also, considerable emphasis above was placed on intention. This does not mean that a detailed and careful analysis must be made before every decision. Following Wittgenstein, and as stated in the Introduction, much of our behaviour may be just an act in the way we have been socially trained. So all action cannot be explained as intentional except that it is an intention to comply with convention. However, *all* actions cannot be explained as socially derived practice. Certainly, we continue to operate to a large extent on socially derived practices and experience, but, on occasion, some event occurs which causes us to go back and question our previously ingrained behaviour.[54] Also, even with socially determined behaviour or other auto-responses, there is still a process between deciding to act, however it is initiated, and the action. This must include a recognition of a situation, when and how to respond, the instructions to act and the taking of action itself. All of this takes place within the brain. No other place exists where this can be located. Although we do not yet know how the brain works for all these processes, it seems possible that *eventually* research may explain much more completely the process of thought, how motives and intentions arise and their link to individual action. However, such an eventual full explanation of the processes in the brain would *not*, in my view, lead to the removal of free will and human intention as some suggest. Much more attention will be paid to all of this in Section 4.

The Nature of the Universe

Now let me turn to consider what science tells us occurs in the world environment around Man, rather than how he evolved. However, as will be seen towards the end of this section, the scientific study of the world around us has also specified the nature of the make-up of Man in an even more fundamental way than the biological viewpoint described above.

It is clear that the development of physics has had major effects upon what we consider our universe to be. In early times men believed the Earth was the centre of the universe. Indeed most of the surface of the Earth was unknown to men. Gradually Man's knowledge of our planet and its place

---

[54] This was also the conclusion I arrived at after studying literature from different disciplines about for the way large corporations approach planning and strategy. See C Tomkins, *Corporate Resource Allocation*, Blackwell, 1991.

in the universe has been expanded – from an awareness of its place in our sun's solar system, to its place in our galaxy, to its place in the universe as developed since the 'Big Bang'. Indeed, I can imagine the existence of a continuing system of multiple universes[55] with continuing 'Big Bangs' as different universes are formed and cease to exist. This development of knowledge is so fundamental that it has had major implications for our perception of our place in the universe(s) and especially for our perception of what God can be, as seen in the next Section of these notes which addresses God and Religion.

Given the success of this approach in increasing our knowledge, it seems quite clear that a reality does exist and Man can measure it. This is really stating little more than the obvious. There is plenty of evidence that our world, our solar system, our galaxy and universe existed before any of the human race came to this planet and, from evidence of those that die, it is obvious that the world, solar system, galaxy and universe will continue after us, both individually and probably also as a human race.

This brings us to the issues of our understanding of time and the physical units and space within our universe. Since the Ancient Greek civilisation, and probably before it, philosophical debate has taken place about whether the world was created at one point of time or has always existed. The former view was obviously adopted later by the authors of the Bible. So, as some ancients used to argue, time began with the creation of the world *as they knew it*. The concept of time, however, and its relation to the universe needs careful analysis.[56]

---

[55] I have no evidence whatever for the existence of such a multiverse, but it does seem feasible and it needs to be contrasted sharply with Everett's theory of multiple universes as a formulation of Quantum mechanics (see S Carroll, *Something Deeply Hidden*, Oneworld, 2019). While I think the concept of a multiverse described in my text above seems at least possible, I find it very difficult to accept that there are many versions of me in different parts of a universal wave function (many worlds) at any time. I can envisage the Everett view that the universe may be made up of just one wave of energy, but that is about as far as my imagination will take me.

[56] Anyone reading this material is reminded again that the objective of these notes is to explore what I think, given my knowledge or perhaps lack of it. I repeat that I am not a scientist. It is obvious that I do not fully understand, for example, Einstein's theories or

First, all humans have an intuitive sense of time. This is based primarily on our lifespan and the awareness that people lived before us and will live after us. We know we were born, we develop and age and we experience events along our life path. While this is a limited human individual's view of time, it does emphasise the basic point that it is change in events and circumstances that give rise to the need for a concept of time so that we can place a relative order on things. We could always say that A occurred before B, but it is useful to have a measure of by how much A preceded B. Apparently, as long ago as 60BC, Lucretius observed that time by itself does not exist: time was dependent on the movement of things.

The concept of time in everyday use is now derived from watches and clocks[57] which are calibrated to measure what we call time in a way that is consistent with regular seasonal and daily cycles of the Earth. For practical use, the yearly cycle of seasons due to the tilt of the Earth as it goes around the sun is divided into months and the daily cycle of the Earth spinning is divided into hours and minutes. A day or a year, however, is not itself a concept of universe-wide time, but a measure of those regular *Earthly* cycles. We may think of them as measures of Earth-time and, for those living on Earth, they are excellent guides for organising our activities. One might note, however, that even if the tilt of the Earth did not exist such that we did not experience seasons (and some parts of the world near the Equator have very small seasonal differences) and if the Earth did not spin so that one side experienced perpetual night while the other enjoyed perpetual day, it would still be possible to talk of time passing as life took place (if it did) and events occurred.[58] We would simply need a different measure of change. So it is important to distinguish between the concept of time itself and ways to measure it.

---

formulae. I have only a layman's view, based on popular literature or TV programmes, of what he and others since him have proved. Nevertheless, my own interpretation of what reality is obviously reflects my own thinking about time and space, however, uninformed that thinking is.

[57] I include clockwork and atomic clocks.

[58] Assuming, that is, life could exist in perpetual day with no seasons – there seems to be no fundamental reason why it should not.

If we were to move to another planet in our solar system, that world would have a different cycle around the sun and a different speed of spinning. Hence, one might conceive of a Venus-time or a Jupiter-time based upon the cycles of those planets. The basic *concept* of time as indicating change would still exist, but the measures used would be different. However, we could still use Earth-years as a measure of duration on Jupiter, but an Earth-year would be only a fraction of the Jupiter year and have no relation to Jupiter's regular cycles. The important point is that, for our practical everyday living activity, we seem to need some stable and regular occurrence external to the observer by means of which to gauge the passage of time.

Most scientists now seem to agree that the universe in which we find ourselves was created with a 'Big Bang' and the date that this occurred can be estimated as so many Earth-years ago. Such a measurement only states that if, since the 'Big Bang', the Earth had existed in its *current* form and with its *current* cyclical behaviour with respect to the Sun (an obvious impossibility), then it would have taken so many billions of current Earth-years to come from the 'Big Bang' to the present time. The expression of time in this way is just making sense of the huge elapse of time for current Earth dwellers using a measure of time with which they are familiar. It is important to note, however, that our clocks or concept of Earth-years are practical tools to help us make sense of our lives, they are not a concept of time itself.

Ancient Man looked upon time beginning with the creation of their perceived world, but now we know that 'our world' extends far beyond Earth to the universe, one might consider time beginning with the 'Big Bang'. But suppose that one were situated out in space with no obvious regular cycle by which to gauge time or, alternatively, many different possibilities for noting regularities upon which to base our measure of time. What measure of time might one use, especially if one wanted to measure extremely long spans of time and have a universe-wide standard of time? Well, alongside the 'Big Bang' theory sits the evidence, since findings using Hubble's telescope, of the expanding universe. If there is no regular planetary cycle to observe,[59] over

---

[59] Apparently galaxies rotate and so, perhaps, that might be used to supply a measure of time.

the very long run we need a different approach to measuring time. It seems to me that this could be done by measuring the distance that the universe has expanded since it was last measured. So the rate of growth in space, if it were stable enough, might then be used as a measure of time. Hence, time would be related to space. Of course, if the universe is expanding at a changing rate, this would not provide a stable measure and, apparently the expansion rate is accelerating again after slowing down for a while. But the rate of change may be too small to imply a significant error considering the purpose for which the measure was made. However, I do not know how practical such a measure would be in terms of both its measurement and what purposes it could serve.

It seems more fruitful for practical operation in space to consider how one would *perceive* both events and time as one moves around within our universe. Moreover, the choice of the type of measurement of time to be used seems trivial compared to the extensive scientific debates about the linked nature of space and time which, obviously, brings us to Einstein. It might be noted here, however, that all scientists are still not agreed about the exact nature of space and time as discussed below.

It is well-known that we cannot always say that what we currently see is occurring *at the present time*. The light from very distant stars has taken millions of years to reach us and, moreover, those stars may no longer exist. Hence our *perception of current reality* may be false. It seems clear, however, from our modern scientific knowledge of how the universe works, that it is simply our *perception* that is time-dated and that the real stars did or still do exist. But our actions are guided by our perceptions and so, if reality is not quite what we see at present, we must be able to understand the link between perception of time and reality in space.

Using the notion just mentioned of the time it takes for light to travel and, following Einstein,[60] it is clear that the faster one travels the slower

---

[60] Here, I cannot overstress stress my paucity of knowledge on this subject. I am also aware that many *philosophical* works have been published on space-time in the late 20th and early 21st centuries. I am nowhere near equipped to deal in detailed way with either the scientific or philosophical developments on this topic. However, one only needs enough in this text to explain the general nature of our universe and our place in it.

time seems to pass. At the limit, people travelling at the speed of light would see that nothing had changed at their point of departure – perception of events transported by light would seem unchanged and, with no events changing, time would be *perceived* as still. That does not mean that nothing has happened since they left. The light from events occurring after they left has not reached them yet. Moreover, someone moving at, say, half the speed of light, would see some events that occurred after they left, but not the events occurring at the moment they looked.[61] A corollary of this is that the fastest that we conceive of time changing is when we are located at the very point where events are changing. We instantly see what is happening.[62] So it is quite clear, as Einstein showed, that our *perception* of time and events in space are a function of how fast we are moving relative to the events being observed and our position in space relative to the events taking place.

His critical insight in 1905 was his Special Theory of Relativity and the realisation that there was no absolute standard for rest against which motion could be measured.[63] It is interesting here to address again the fundamental question of whether there is a reality outside of human perception because it has just been argued that what a human *sees* as real depends on time, speed and space. But events will be taking place even where there is no longer human observation and there is plenty of evidence that the universe existed before Man strode the Earth. One can still have a notion of how events change with time without human observation.

While my understanding of the science of space-time may be very limited, I am aware that Einstein with his Special Theory of Relativity[64] extended

---

[61] This assumes, of course, that the distance travelled is significant enough to cause a perceptible delay between events and their observation.

[62] This assumes that nothing can travel faster than light and time-travel is impossible. See Stephen Hawking, *Space and Time Warps*, public lecture, 1999 for an analysis of this issue (available as www.hawking.org.uk/space-and-time-warps.html).

[63] Einstein also showed, in his later General Relativity Theory, how clocks run slower on Earth than in space due to the weaker gravitational force on the clock in space.

[64] The Special Theory of Relativity refers to the special case where objects travel at constant velocities. The later General Theory of Relativity allows for objects to accelerate, which, Einstein said, gave rise to gravity.

this line of thinking to say that neither time nor space existed separately: the measurement of time cannot be independent of the movement of matter.[65] Subsequently, Minkowski, one of Einstein's former teachers, found that everything in the Special Theory could be explained in geometrical terms if time was taken as a fourth dimension along with the usual three physical dimensions. This four-dimensional geometrical model became known as spacetime.[66]

Subsequently, Einstein was working to relax the assumption of constant velocity of objects in his Special Theory to allow acceleration of them, when he realised that acceleration and gravity are the equivalent of each other. 'If you were standing on a platform being accelerated through space, you would feel held down by your own weight in a gravitational field.'[67] This led to his other significant breakthrough with his General Theory of Relativity, which is a theory of gravity and not just motion. Moreover, non-Euclidian geometry developed earlier by Riemann and Clifford,[68] was now being used to model his theory. This all gave rise to Einstein's concept of a curved four-dimensional model of spacetime as a description of the whole universe, by which gravity was explainable by the curvature of space. The curvature seems intuitively consistent with the much later acceptance that the space is like a closed ball[69] with three dimensions derived from the initial explosion of the 'Big Bang'.[70]

---

[65] My intuitive understanding of this is that one cannot say where an object is without specifying a point of time, but time itself is merely a description of movement of matter, hence time and the three-dimensional space are intertwined.

[66] See J Gribbin, *Einstein's Masterwork 1915 and the General Theory of Relativity*, Icon Books Ltd, 2015, p 115 for an intuitive explanation of the implications of this.

[67] J Gribbin, *Einstein's Masterwork*, op cit, p 118.

[68] See Gribbin, op cit, once more. Traditional Euclidian geometry dealt with flat surfaces, non-Euclidian geometry dealt with curved surfaces.

[69] Possibly with knobs on as suggested by Clifford, see Gribbin, op cit, once more, p 145.

[70] General Relativity Theory also apparently indicates that the initial conditions present when the 'Big Bang' occurred completely determine every event since. If we are uncertain about some forthcoming event, that is only because we do not have perfect knowledge of all factors that will influence it. In such a state, as Einstein said in the 1920s 'There is no such

So, for better or worse, that is my understanding of Einstein's theories and their implications for our understanding of the nature of our universe. On the other hand, while Einstein may have said that there is no such thing as the notion of time held by the philosopher, he presumably meant within his conception of mathematical physics. Time is clearly not a physical element. It is really a construct recording the pace of change and the construct we humans use is one which fits in with our own context on this world. There is, therefore, a very valid concept of time in *philosophy*. We, and I believe Einstein himself, would have been be hard pushed to operate in life without it.

Having reached this conclusion, I then learned, from some introductory reading about Quantum Field Theory (QFT),[71] that Einstein himself did

---

thing as the time of the philosopher' and later in 1953, just before he died, the 'distinction between past, present and future is only a stubbornly persistent illusion'. It is said, however, (see Gisin referenced below) that Einstein himself was uneasy with such a conclusion based on the mathematics, but that we probably had to live with it. However, this deterministic view of reality has been challenged by quantum physics and developments in that field may lead to a revision of this four-dimension continuum which encompasses the past, present and future. In addition, a very recent paper by Nicolas Gisin, a Swiss physicist (*Classical and intuitionalist mathematical languages shape our understanding of time in physics, Group of Applied Physics, University of Geneva, 8 April 2020*) suggests that a move to intuitional mathematics could help free physics from its determinism and lead to a view of time that was more in tune with our everyday sense of what time is. At a more general level of argument, the four-dimensional/curved concept of space arose out of the way the theory of gravity was modelled mathematically. Mathematics may offer good predictions, but it is not, necessarily, a depiction of what reality actually is. Finally, while the discovery of whether we have a determinate or indeterminate universe will, no doubt, lead to many advances in Man's achievements, one wonders whether it matters very much which is correct in terms of the way we need to use a notion of time in our everyday lives. Whatever theory proves to be correct, we will see change around us and we will need a concept of time as a practical tool, however we decide to measure it.

[71] R A Brooks, *Fields of Colour: the theory that escaped Einstein*, Epsilon Publishers, 3rd edition, 2016. My comments on QFT here are based significantly on Brooks' book. It seems that most physicists now accept QFT as a preferred basis for theorising about the universe, although some argue that it is not necessary and that adequate predictions can be made by simpler means. I am also very aware that my views on QFT are based almost wholly on a book written in non-rigorous form for laymen like me who do not have a deep knowledge of science, although I have sought a number of other sources to try to check my understanding, such as S Carroll, *Something Deeply Hidden*, op cit.

not actually adopt that view of reality and that he thought that gravity was a force field. If so, his view of reality was quite consistent with QFT and, according to QFT, space is the same three-dimensional form with which we are all familiar and time is also exactly what we intuitively believe – merely a measure of that physical change.

> In this chapter we will see that in QFT (and also in Einstein's theory) there is no eerie fourth dimension: space is space and time is time. We will also see that gravity is caused by a force field – not curvature, and, that, contrary to popular belief, QFT is compatible with General Relativity.[72]

I was interested to learn that. If this statement is correct, it made me far more comfortable with my own intuition about time and space, but then I had to try to understand at least some basic aspects of QFT.

QFT re-emphasises that the space in our universe is not empty, but consists of fields: five force fields and two matter fields.[73] A field[74] is a condition of an area of space, within which can be specified the strength of gravity, electromagnetism or other force according to the type of field being considered (see footnote). For example, it is well known that the gravitational pull lessens as one moves away from an object like Earth. The

---

[72] RA Brooks, op cit.

[73] Under some specifications there are 17 fields. Brooks describes seven fields as follows. The Force Fields are: Gravity (the attraction possessed by every object in the universe which interacts with every other object; its quanta are Gravitons), the Electromagnetic Field (which only interacts with charged fields; its quanta are Photons), the Strong Field (that holds the nucleus of an atom together; its quanta are Pions), the Weak Field (present within the nucleus which can change neutrons into protons; its quanta are W+, W- and Z-0) and the Higgs Field (which slows down quanta moving through space; its quanta are Higgs boson). The two Matter Fields are: the Lepton Field (whose quanta are electrons, etc.) and the Baryon Field (whose quanta are protons, neutrons, etc.). Both these fields do not give out forces themselves, but can create and be acted upon by force fields. A detailed understanding of this is not relevant for the reference to QFT that I will make in this text and I could not provide it.

[74] One analogous view of a field is a room where every point has a variation of temperature. This would be the field of temperature. Space can be envisaged as comprising 17 (or seven if you prefer it) fields flowing amongst each other. Another analogy is of an ocean filled with multiple fluids rather than just water.

quanta,[75] in this case gravitons, are spread out over a wider area and so the strength of the pull weakens.[76] The central thrust of QFT, however, is that solid particles do not exist. All matter, the 'hard stuff' all around us and gases, are comprised of atoms which in turn consist of the nucleus (formed of protons and neutrons) and electrons, all of which are field excitations or quanta. They are not solid particles; these quanta are chunks of energy and are not in one continuous stream.[77] Human beings are also matter and so it can now be seen why I said above that the science of the universe around us, as well as biology and our theories of evolution, explains what we are made of.

So, how can one think of space? As QFT explains, space in our universe is not an empty void, but filled with overlapping fields. Presumably these fields were derived as configurations of energy given to us by the 'Big Bang'.[78] Ostensibly beyond our universe is a void which is empty and which existed before our universe was created and into which our universe is expanding.

This last argument will need to be modified if it is eventually proved that there are multiple universes in a much larger system, periodically exploding, expanding, contracting and reverting to a core, point-like, mass. Perhaps they are even overlapping. This would imply a continuing, perhaps everlasting, *multiverse*.[79] Aristotle may have thought that the world (Earth) had existed for ever and, generally, that is now taken as wrong, but with a multiuniverse

---

[75] Einstein was quite familiar with the concept of quanta. Indeed, his spectacular year of work in 1905 was responsible for laying part of the foundation for later Quantum Theory.

[76] Although if one moves back within the Earth towards the centre, the gravitational pull also lessens because the pull of gravity from different parts of the Earth counteract each other.

[77] This means that Rutherford's widely used picture of an atom consisting of a nucleus surrounded by electrons as particles orbiting the nucleus is misleading. A QFT-based picture would show the nucleus surrounded by a short-range field representing The Strong Field within the larger electromagnetic field which has no hard border. Hence, the atom likewise has no hard boundary; it consists of fields as described.

[78] There are also some scientists who question whether the 'Big Bang' occurred.

[79] Defined here as a collection or group of universes. This may seem a little illogical from a linguistic point of view, because the term universe presumably means to include everything, whereas I am now saying that our universe may only be one of many.

reality, the phenomenon of much broader concept of perpetual reality may need to be reviewed.

However, it is not the intention of a text of this nature to form a view as to whether Einstein's four-dimensional model or QFT or any other model gives a better description of our real universe. What these theories do provide, and surely each has a large degree of reality behind them, is a picture that indicates the general nature and complexity of the environment within which we live and must be taken into account in examining our philosophies.

At the very least it is clear that our universe is much more complex seen from the early 21st century than it was even in the early 20th centuries and before. If our conception of our real universe can change so much, then surely this impacts upon how Man sees his status and identity within the universe. Moreover, this change in scientific knowledge is not, of course, complete. Many theories seem to abound waiting to be tested rigorously about the nature of the universe (more aspects of quantum physics, String theory – where the quanta are strings rather than 'blobs', wormholes, even more informed speculation about time travel, ten-dimensional space, etc.). It would be interesting to know what the established view will be on all this in 100 years' time. Will the *Theory of Everything* be specified and proven? Not long ago Stephen Hawking thought we would relatively soon have such a theory, but he changed his mind[80] and then thought that we will never have it. Hence, we may never have an absolutely complete philosophy of reality, but our understanding of it changes as new research reveals more about that reality.[81] This applies to both our position in the universe and the internal functioning of our bodies and what they consist of. If a Theory of Everything is to be sought, both aspects must be considered.

All this dalliance with science may seem rather distant from my initial objective of identifying 'personal philosophies' which influence my

---

[80] Stephen Hawking, *Godel and the end of physics*, public lecture, 2002 (available at www.hawking.org.uk/godel-and-the-end-of-physics.html).

[81] Some scientists say that we can never have a Theory of Everything until we have solved the mystery of human consciousness. This will be addressed, but not solved, in Section 4.

behaviour. But it is very relevant. My perception of the reality of the cosmos and, my understanding of how we evolved and, indeed, how we are formed from packets of energy just like all other matter, must, at the very least, influence my view of God and Religion as addressed in the Section 3 and may well be relevant in considering Consciousness in Section 4 and Ethics in Section 5. Also some philosophers[82] are questioning the basis of our evolution as described earlier. I, therefore, felt Section 2 needed a discussion of science as a foundation for discussion of philosophical issues.

---

[82] e.g. Nagel and Midgley, op cit.

3.

God and Religion

While the limited amount of philosophical literature that I have read often addresses God and Religion together, I wish to treat them as separate concepts. In this exercise, God refers to an all-powerful, omniscient 'being',[83] whereas I see Religion as a human *practice* to incorporate any of the faiths adopted in this world such as Christian, Moslem or Buddhist. The question of whether God exists is to ask whether God is real; that is does God have a *physical* existence?[84] This is a legitimate question. In contrast, it is quite obvious that Religion is a real practice, even though it has a variety of forms and interpretations. Although it seems to me that this distinction is not often highlighted by religious leaders, one who did make a sharp distinction between God and Religion was Paine.[85] In one of the most savage critiques of Western religions ever written, he indicated that he was a believer in God (he was a Deist) although he advocated scrapping all Western religions (except possibly Quakerism). As seen later, it is clear that I feel that he may have got this the wrong way round, but God and Religion do need to be addressed separately to understand any person's philosophy. Many may run the two concepts together in expressing a view on their philosophy on these subjects, but, to get a full understanding, one should examine their view of God and Religion separately.

---

[83] Or, to recognise the alternative to monotheism, a set of all-powerful beings.

[84] As seen in section 2 this does not have to mean a hard physical existence as we perceive it in everyday life. Fundamentally, all matter consists of energy.

[85] T Paine, *The Age of Reason*. Paine was of considerable influence with his views on both politics and religion in the late 18th century. As will become clear later, my philosophy is almost the reverse of Paine's. I am not a Deist, but I do believe in the value of religion when properly handled. We shall, however, need to refer to him again in the Section on Political philosophy. He was very influential in debates about the French Revolution and had a major impact on the formation of the then newly independent America

On the Existence of God

Why begin with God? Much of philosophical literature, especially from earlier centuries, attempts to link the then understanding of our world with the presence of a God or Gods. In striving to understand what our world is and how it is organised and works, the failure to have a rational answer beyond the notion that someone must have designed it was paramount. As humans we ourselves were the most intelligent beings we knew and we also knew that we were not capable of intelligent design on such a scale. Consequently, some greater 'being' must have done it and efforts were made through elaborate argument to prove that God exists – perhaps the most well-known being Anselm's ontological argument. This question of whether God exists or not needs to be addressed first before considering the validity of Religion in general or specific religious faiths in particular.

To address the question of whether God exists it is helpful, to me at least, to start with Darwin's concept of evolution and also Neo-Darwinian thought. Darwin argued how each species evolved through adaptation to its environment. It is important to understand exactly what this means. As Dawkins[86] makes very clear, evolution did not take place as a conscious adaptation,[87] but by means of random variations in genetic make-up with the result that those beings with the variation that best suited their environment overcame or outlasted their less fortunate rivals in the competition for food and procreation. To this one can add my earlier arguments about the role of Genetic Drift and Recombination, as explained by Wagner, and organisms' intentions and events in establishing the current diversity of life on Earth.

A large part of this was a continuing process which took place from the earliest of life forms on this planet until the present day.[88] Nothing in this

---

[86] R Dawkins, *The Selfish Gene*, Oxford University Press, 1976.

[87] This view may need considerable revision in future as man is becoming increasingly able to undertake conscious genetic manipulation himself.

[88] Paine, op cit, declared that for him the evidence that God existed was nature itself and that it must have been a super-intelligence that created it. He argues that no earthly being can create itself. Each was created by its parents and one can trace back the line of parentage until one arrives at the first being. Someone, he thinks God, must have created that first being.

argument establishes that God does not exist. God could have designed this evolutionary process and imposed it upon the world. Also, even if God did not, it does not explain how life began. Did God initiate life on Earth? Did he create the first cell and first virus? And, indeed, did God create the universe? As explained in the section on Physics, the accepted view now is that there was a beginning to our Universe[89] and that it has not existed forever. Embryonic theories exist about how this could have occurred under the laws of Physics, but it is still possible to argue that these laws themselves were created by God. Hence, we are unable completely to discount the existence of a super-intelligence called God. There is no proof that God exists or does not exist and so it would seem that the sensible stance is to be agnostic. But those seeking to increase knowledge should not leave matters at this very general level of conclusion. If Man had simply stopped and accepted the position every time he faced a situation where he thought 'I will never understand this', there would have been little advancement of knowledge.

If one adopts an agnostic stance, *one should try to establish much more precisely what one is uncertain about.* An agnostic living centuries ago might have thought that God might exist in a physical form somewhere just above the clouds. Subsequent science has shown that to be impossible. A would-be agnostic now should press on to ask, given current knowledge, what form could God take if he (she or it) does exist. So, while God as a supreme universal intelligence may exist, the realm of possibility within which God may exist has been radically reduced by advances in physical science over the last two or three centuries and this process is likely to continue.

It is relevant to trace the evolving nature of God as perceived by Man. Earlier Man did not view the world as ordered by a monotheistic God, but by a series of gods often linked with key life-giving elements – including the Sun. There was a variation in the attributes of the gods in different parts

---

Paine was writing, however, before developments in evolution theory or modern views on the origin of the universe. It would be interesting to know what Paine would have written if he were alive now.

[89] As argued earlier there may be other universes. Many universes may have *always* existed within a process by which universes are continually being created, expanding and eventually dying. This would be quite consistent with our universe having a definite point of creation.

of the world. In due course, the view developed in the main monotheistic religions was that there was just one God (albeit a Three-in-One in the case of Christianity). God was often portrayed with a similar image to Man and still is by some religions. So our understanding of God has evolved and, given what was stated in the last Section about the nature of the universe or the possibility of multiple universes, it is clear that one cannot make any absolute statement about the existence or otherwise of God. The concept of God is still evolving.

God *could* exist outside of our universe or even outside a system of multiple universes. Our knowledge does not extend far enough to be able to determine finally the nature of our universe, let alone decide confidently whether there is a God who created and is overseeing all this. As stated already, the best we can be is agnostic. What we can say, however, is that, at the very least and despite Christian orthodoxy, it is *most unlikely* that Man exists in God's image. Given our current knowledge of the universe, it must be concluded that Man must now see himself as a mere speck situated on another speck, the Earth, in a massive universe or series of universes. Man has only existed as a species for a very small amount of time compared to the life of the Earth, let alone the life of the universe(s), and is himself evolving. Why should a God impose his image on such a transient Man?

So, it seems quite obvious from our knowledge of the universe now that a God in the form of Man does not exist.[90] One should not be agnostic about that. It is, however, a valid agnostic position to argue that there could, *in theory*, be a God or 'Intelligence' which has a quite unknown physical form or spirit beyond our ken. For example, as stated above, this *could* exist beyond our universe or system of multiple universes. One might then see our universe(s) as a cell or series of cells controllable, to some extent, by an external force which we can call God. Alternatively, God might, *in theory*, exist in some spiritual form *around us and within our universe and, perhaps, even within our human structure*, while being beyond our perception. This might not be as odd as it seems. Man lived for years quite unaware of radio waves. The earlier review of QFT showed how the

---

[90] Or Man in the form of God.

universe consists of energy fields as the basis for everything and suggests that all matter including ourselves are formed of just balls of energy. So it would not be too outrageous to suggest that God could be a field of energy that has not 'crystallised' itself into physical form. Could God exist in a wraith-like form of super-energy field as yet to be discovered? Could such a concept of God have an intelligence? If so, God might even be intertwined with our consciousness to influence our lives. Is it possible that, as William James argued, the source of religion was human feeling and not reason.[91] If this is correct, could the human feelings of guilt or self-approbation be derived from an evaluative process imposed on our consciousness by such a GOD-like field? Of course, with our current state of knowledge, it is impossible to know. My own view, however, is that it is highly improbable.

It seems quite acceptable that many may not want to explore the question of a God's existence too closely for fear of the implications if they decide that God does not exist when he/she does exist. Also, it is quite clear that many *do* get considerable consolation from their belief in God, especially when thinking about death, sickness or bereavement. If this enables people to cope with adversity, there is a clear advantage to the practice. It is, however, the *belief* in God which creates the required comfort, whether that belief is (eventually) shown to be right or wrong. It is as though the brain is controlling its own mind to think in a given way so as not to be too distraught. It is quite clear that we do at times tell ourselves to dismiss thoughts of mishap or disaster in order to get on with life and not be inhibited by fear of what would be unfortunate events. Is this, fundamentally, any different from taking consolation from prayer and belief in God?

Others may simply not want to think about it at all and say, by way of bypassing the subject, that one cannot know if God exists and so there is no point in thinking about it. Nevertheless, if one *does* want to think about it, one should take into account what we now *do* know about the form that God *cannot* take and then consider what possible forms remain. I remain an agnostic, but only because I cannot prove that the more exotic forms of super intelligence discussed in the previous paragraphs do not exist. In

[91] See Kenny, *Philosophy in the Modern World*, op cit, p 312.

addition, I am prepared to take a probabilistic approach and say it is most unlikely that God exists even in these exotic forms, rather than insisting on a definitive answer. There are very few situations in life where there is *absolute* certainty of outcome.

Even if a super intelligence exists beyond our universe or as some ethereal sprit within it, it seems difficult to imagine that it hears literally every individual's prayers or contributes to life on Earth and a personal life hereafter in the way various religions through their actions seem to claim. Based on such thoughts, I think that it is *highly unlikely* that such an intelligence exists, although I cannot prove it. God did not create Man. Man 'created' at first many and then one 'true' God in each monotheistic religion. Man did this to help himself make sense of his situation. If I am wrong and God does exist, it must be such an exotic form from our human viewpoint that it does not get involved in the lives of us *individual* 'specks' and I need not be over concerned about God in organising my own life. Religions do, however, definitely exist. They are real *human practices*, and may well be very relevant to organising my life and so religion needs separate consideration.

Religion

While religions may have become established through recognising the limited powers of Man and the felt need for supernatural support, religions still do have an established place in society. The main religions of the world have a very strong influence on many people's lives. One may or may not view them, like Marx, as 'the opium of the people'. In his view religions were administered by the elite to stop their subjects from fretting too much about life's problems and promising everlasting happiness in return for obeying the their guidelines. Yet religious practice is still widely observed, even by those not so easily duped. Actions of religious leaders worldwide have often seemed self-seeking in maintaining their own power, influence and standard of living, both historically and currently – either directly or by supporting the current ruling elite. Religions and even factions within the main religions have competed directly by way of wars, persecution and violence which do not seem in keeping with religious teaching. Indeed, one often wonders whether the apparent religious differences are not a means of justifying conflicts where they would have occurred anyway as different groups, races or regional peoples seek to increase or maintain power. One might conclude, therefore, that much evil has been and is currently being undertaken in the name of religion, especially by extremist groups. Moreover, throughout history this has not been confined to just one religious group. These range from the atrocities in Europe (including England) when Catholics and Protestants persecuted each other with fearful death sentences to the current feuds *between* Moslem sects. One is also mindful of Paine's[92] demolition of the idea that the main religions are revelations about God through the main holy books of each religion. In particular, he devoted many pages analysing in detail both the Old and New Testaments and makes a very persuasive case that those texts serve the interests of the authors who were clearly not God. Also he argues that these authors could not possibly have had a special access to God to serve as a channel through which God communicated.

Despite all this, all the main religions do have a prescription for how life should be lived and much of that recommended seems to illustrate a good guideline for living. Gamble et al.[93] argue that religion developed as a necessary device to create order in social networks gaining in size – and thereby creating a sense of identity beyond the immediate local group. They, therefore, probably started to develop in emergent form at least 100,000 years ago. Much later, all the main religions were spearheaded by charismatic individuals who in their different ways were leaders of men claiming a unique and direct access to God and, therefore, able, in their own justification, to declare how human beings should live. So religions, in more embryonic form existed long before Christ, Mohammed, etc., and *preceded* national governments as a means of creating social order. For centuries, when this was virtually the only guideline,[94] the main religions ensured that there was some collaboration, coordination and civilisation in society where otherwise chaos and brutishness would have reigned.

---

[92] Paine, op cit.

[93] C Gamble, J Gowlett and R Dunbar, *Thinking Big*, Thames & Hudson, 2014.

[94] There were other guidelines, e.g. Aristotle's Eudaimian Ethics.

The majority who practice a religion at the current time do not support extremist actions (and associated violence) and probably do not question too closely the fundamental matter of whether their God exists or hears their prayers, or reveals his truth through the Bible, Koran, etc. What they probably do is remain involved in this *human practice* and support it for the evident good which comes from observing most of its recommendations on how we should live. They see religion as important in its dominant, if not the only, form of philosophical discussion of what is right and wrong. Apart from priests, people probably do not worry too much about its theological foundations.

I conclude, therefore, that all religions as practised now have very shaky theological foundations, but they also house many desirable social and cultural traits relevant for designing a wholesome earthly functioning. The main religions also move beyond giving advice on how to live one's life and take positive actions to support the less privileged. Much good socially is derived from many religious practices. Modern Man ought to be able to construct guidelines for living practice (and does in framing laws and rules of expected behaviour) without trying to justify them by reference to an All-seeing, Omnipotent God. The Humanist movement intends to do just that. But, if we treat the question of God's existence and its associated theology as a separate matter, Humanism is no more than a type of religion attempting to map out how we should live.

In fact, the repeated reference to theological underpinning and God by religious leaders in order to justify their advice on social practice actually *undermines* their messages. As a recent example (January 2015) Dr Sentamu, the then Archbishop of York, in arguing along with other Christian leaders that there needs to be more attention paid to ameliorating the plight of the poor, stated:

> If God has created us unique, (and) all of us have got his image and likeness, is it ever right that I should have more when somebody else has nothing?[95]

---

[95] Personally, I would prefer a goal which placed more stress on equality of opportunity rather than equal wealth amongst everyone, although there is also a place for debate about the relative distribution of wealth.

His argument to help the poor was very welcome, but he should not justify it by reference to the suspect truth about how God created us. There was no need to do so. His argument would carry more weight amongst more of the population if he addressed statistics showing exactly how wealth and welfare varied and what problems and difficulties that caused. That would be more likely to encourage intelligent debate on both the creation and distribution of wealth and welfare. The Archbishop also seemed to ignore, in this statement, how life in general and human progress in particular has evolved.[96]

In addition to valuable guidance of how society should operate, observance of religion may also offer benefits at the personal psychological level. I remember walking home from church as a boy feeling quite uplifted after attending a church service – probably mainly through participating in singing songs of joy which led to a surge in bodily endorphins! Also, as a boy, I gained considerable comfort from daily private praying, particularly in respect of my father who was seriously ill throughout my childhood. I later came to view this as self-deception, but the feeling of comfort and well-being was real[97] at the time and sustained me through my childhood.

Perhaps a distinction should be made between two types of prayer – public and private. For example, for the Christian attending church, the participation in prayer may, for some, be just a social act. It is what one does if one is part of that religious society and one wants to remain part of that society for social and cultural reasons. Undertaking private prayer on the other hand would seem to indicate that the supplicant believes he or she is being heard and that there is a good chance of a response – otherwise why do it? Would one gain comfort from such praying if one thought it was just a human ritual? Perhaps one would. Possibly this would be through the notion of forgiveness for sins. Does the very practice of admitting one's sins

---

[96] Perhaps it is unfair to judge him on one random statement. His reading and education clearly extends far beyond that implied. I use this example merely to illustrate that, in my view, one should not base social or political policy on just questionable theological dogma.

[97] Participation in hymn singing and even attendance at church itself may be viewed in this way.

and regretting them, even just to oneself, have the effect of coming to terms with them and be part of the process of changing behaviour in future?

Alternatively, if the prayer is more concerned with the welfare of others, as mine was regarding my father, does the prayer focus attention such that one then concentrates on acting in a better way to help that 'other'? I have no idea, but there seems to be scope for establishing good reasons for following a formal religion as a human practice, even if one does not believe that there is a God. Even so, my view is that it is pretty certain that a God as portrayed in the main religious books does not exist. Religions ought to be able to fashion advice on living a good, decent and honourable life without practising religious rituals and declarations made by leading religious authorities insisting on linking such behaviour to an Almighty.

As I thought about my interpretation of religion in order to write this section, I could not ignore the terrible *Charlie Hebdo* massacre which dominated the press and Western news several years ago. That attack was undertaken by religious extremists in France to gain revenge for the publication of mocking cartoons of the prophet Mohammed. It was very welcome that all religious leaders, including Moslems, have condemned this action, but some, including the Pope, have stressed that if one mocks another's religion it is not surprising if it leads to violence, in the same way, the Pope said, as might an insult of one's mother.

His statement is sensible. One always should exercise care not to give offence where people's deep-seated feelings are involved, but this should not be taken to prohibit intelligent and polite debate about both the theological bases and current practices of different religions as well as sensitive issues on immigration from different communities. Dr Sentamu, Archbishop of York, stated, after his argument mentioned above, that the question of the appropriate level and form of immigration into the UK should be the subject of intelligent debate and not assertion. He seemed to fail to see the inconsistency between his worthy stance on this topic and his assertions, without debate, about how God created us all equal.

Intelligent debates over theological themes have taken place between and within religions for centuries. It would be paradoxical if such debate were looked upon with disfavour as more and more is discovered about the world we live in and what we humans are. As knowledge and society develops, religions wanting their social role to continue must be prepared to defend their theologies in rigorous debate or be prepared to forgo them in favour of alternative rationales. One is reminded of Nietzsche's view that the idea of a moral law without a lawgiver (i.e. God) is vacuous, suggesting that there cannot be an alternative rationale and that religion, therefore, is without foundation. However, religion can have a legitimate lawgiver that is not God. Moral rules and ethics have been developed through social evolution (as discussed later in Section 5). Man, collectively, has acted as lawgiver based on experience of what is desirable. I feel sure that religions will evolve yet further just as other social practices have. As Man's knowledge increases, doubtful theological foundations must evolve if they are to gain continuing acceptance of religion as a useful guideline of how to live one's life.[98]

---

[98] This discussion focused mainly on Christianity and Islam, but I am sure that the general nature of it applies equally to other religions.

4.

Metaphysics and Philosophy of the Mind

It is quite apparent, from even the limited summaries and references to the history of philosophy that I have accessed, that I do not have the knowledge to attempt a synthesis of the mass of literature relating to Metaphysics from Ancient Greece to the current day. I have argued previously, however, that I do not need to have a comprehensive knowledge of any of these themes in philosophy if my objective is simply to explore what I think given *my* current knowledge and situation. I will, however, relate these thoughts to a few philosophers and scientists that have written on this topic in recent years.

The concept of Metaphysics seems very difficult to define. As I understand it, it concerns a search for establishing first principles involved in understanding reality and our human place within it. It, hence, seems to stand hierarchically above truths derived from the scientific (Realist/ materialistic) method of physical science in the sense that Metaphysics itself provides a view on what phenomena are accessible and understandable by means of physical science. Metaphysics includes topics such as the nature of the universe (ontology), the nature of being, identity, the mind and matter (philosophy of the mind), God, religion and spirituality. My view on ontology is covered in Appendix 3 at the end of this text and to some extent in Section 2. God and religion deserved a separate Section 3 in this pamphlet. Here I will address the other topics mentioned, but they are run together as I find my thoughts about them overlap considerably.

The nature of being addresses the issue of what it is to be alive. I am pretty sure how I got here. Darwin, amongst others, convinced us that we arrived through a long process of evolution and, more recently, Dawkins[99]

---

[99] Richard Dawkins, *The Ancestor's Tale*, Weidenfeld & Nicolson, 2004.

produced an impressive mapping of the path of evolution undertaken from the earliest forms of life to arrive at the current human race. We can also differentiate ourselves from other animals by observing our different bodily attributes. That is not, however, an explanation of what it is like *to be human*. How does a human being know that he or she is alive? What, fundamentally, is it like to be alive? The answer must lie in an understanding of what consciousness is.[100]

At its basic level, consciousness means just being aware[101] of something, but it is much more than that, although people define it differently and some say they do not know what it is. In my view consciousness includes awareness, memory, thinking, understanding, reason, choice of action and the question of free will. All of these are intertwined in my feeling of consciousness. I become aware of something, some of it goes into my memory bank (if only temporarily), I think about it and gain a better understanding which in itself changes my awareness of the matter. I may then evaluate my position and whether I need to take action, consider the alternatives, to some extent based on my memory, and make a choice which may or may not be a free choice. At every stage there is a feedback to awareness and understanding and I will be conscious of what is happening. For purposes of exploration in more depth of what I think consciousness is,

---

[100] There is, of course, a distinction between consciousness and self-consciousness. The former is an awareness that there is something 'out there' beyond me and what it is like to exist as a separate being. Self-consciousness is usually taken to mean embarrassment or discomfort. Obviously, it is the former that I address in these notes.

[101] David Chalmers in *The Conscious Mind*, Oxford University Press, 1996 initially refers to awareness as the availability of information for report or control of behaviour. He then later (p 229) modifies the definition to information that is available for consideration for a wide range of behavioural processes. Clearly, just the availability of information does not mean that one is conscious of it. I prefer in this text to define awareness in a more everyday sense – that is to mean any act of consciousness. In other words one must be conscious to be aware of something and if one is not conscious there is no awareness of the information that is available. Clearly, following Wittgenstein, factors may affect our behaviour without us being particularly conscious of them, but I prefer here to exclude such factors from my understanding of awareness. More attention to the role information plays in the operation of the Mind will be considered later in this Section.

I will discuss the topic of awareness separately and then move onto to the other aspects of consciousness.

Awareness and Memory

First, it is obvious that I have bodily organs which sense various physical phenomena. These are sight, hearing, touch, taste and smell. When it sees things, hears things, touches things, etc., my body records the sensation and, usually, has some form of reaction. Any reaction must be based, to a large extent, on memory of previous sensation. The initial reactions may often seem to be a mechanistic response in the way a thermostat operates which might suggest that my body is not that of a live animal. However, the fact that usually I have choice of reaction to a sensation,[102] whatever the sensation felt, is evidence of being alive. This notion of choice relates centrally to the philosophy of the Mind and will be further examined later in this Section in addressing the topics of Reason and Free Will.

Awareness, however, involves a lot more than the receipt of basic messages from the sensory organs mentioned above. I can remember, as a young boy, frightening myself with the realisation that one day I would no longer exist.[103] I would lie awake trying to ignore any sensations such a sight, sound, touch and yet still try to see how, without thinking about anything else, I could be aware that I was alive. (Perhaps we all do that.) I can still do that, although it no longer frightens me. When I do attempt this, I feel two things. First, I hear/feel my heart beating as it pumps blood around my body, but I feel more than that. I find it difficult to put into words, but I also have a sense that my brain is functioning and this sense seems quite distinct from the primary sensory organs just listed. The brain is still being employed to think even if I (that is my brain) has told myself to think of nothing. It seems blank, but still giving out a message that it is on standby and can be operated when needed. A crude likeness might be a blank computer

---

[102] Obviously this is not always the case. For example, if I sustain a massive injury, my body will react without much contemplation.

[103] This must be felt at some time by just about every human being.

screen turned on and ready to be activated and used when I wish. It is there shimmering, waiting to be used. However, there is obviously a major difference. The computer screen is outside of me and could be used by me or others. The 'screen' of my brain is within and part of me and can only be used by me. Provided my body is currently supported by the main bodily organs, my brain *can activate itself* and become conscious of other matters when it chooses. The core of awareness that one is alive must, therefore, be in the brain. According to Searle,[104] Wittgenstein made a mistake in saying very little about the brain in his approach to the philosophy of the Mind. The beating heart has a central part to play in allowing one to recognise that one is alive and it does have a physical regulating mechanism, but it does not have a *thinking* awareness mechanism itself. I become aware of its operation via sound and touch sensations which are in turn interpreted by the brain. The heart is just a bodily engine, not a centre of emotion or thought. Like other key organs such as the liver and kidneys, its effective operation is a prerequisite to existence, but it serves the brain by supplying blood to it – the *awareness* of being alive is situated in the brain.

The recognition that one exists does not depend only upon the obvious sensations noted by the prime sensory organs (i.e. touch, sound, sight or taste). Nor does it depend on just the awareness of having a brain which is active. There are emotions like love, fear, joy, hate, disgust, etc. These may be reactions to signals from the sensory organs, but they are separable from them. They are based on beliefs and dispositions based on experience and held in the brain which may then initiate physical bodily actions. Moreover, as Man evolved beyond the need to focus all his energies on sustenance and survival, he had spare time, but the brain was still functioning and, perhaps because of its physical construction, could not remain idle. If awake, the brain has no alternative but to be functioning at some level. This led, I believe, to the development of 'entertaining activities' or what might be called 'higher level human satisfactions'. Examples are the feeling of satisfaction from making something, writing a book or creating or enjoying art; from not just playing a game, but of winning it; from understanding

---

[104] J Searle, see p 344 of Bryan Magee, *The Great Philosophers*, BBC Books, 1987.

something such as solving a crossword puzzle, a mathematical equation or scientific mystery; from helping others, undertaking charitable activities or making donations.[105] These may all involve the use of prime sense organs and physical activity in generating a 'joy of doing', but the initiation of the search for such satisfactions and the subsequent satisfaction derived from an evaluation of achievement seems to be a separate reaction in the brain. It is a *combination* of the physical and mental in providing a 'joy of doing' and post-satisfaction that determines whether the human finds the activity attractive or will be repeated.

There is also a distinctive part of awareness which is exclusively human and that arises through use of language. This is not all that language does (see Section 9), but it does enable an enhanced level of awareness concerning events beyond our immediate experience including other persons' views and arguments like those considered in this pamphlet. Indeed, our awareness can then be interpreted as knowledge held in the memory. This will include knowing where such information can be found if it is not currently held in the brain.

It may be concluded that human consciousness at its basic level is the brain being aware of existence and signals from sensory organs together with a recognition that my brain is always switched on. But it is also being aware of what I have termed higher satisfactions and what can be gleaned through the use of language via the media, conversation and literature. Moreover, medical experts are making progress in showing how the electrical signals relating to these 'satisfactions' are interpreted within the cerebral cortex and its constituent lobes.[106] Scientists now know which parts of the brain are

---

[105] All these activities may also, of course, result in dissatisfaction.

[106] In discussing consciousness, it is often asked whether animals possess this attribute and, if so, what is it like to be a cat or a dog or a sheep. We humans can never know this because we do not have brains like cats, dogs or sheep, but we can be assured that animals do have some degree of self-awareness. Their physical behaviour is determined, like ours, by an interaction between the brain and operational aspects of their bodies. Their brains are not as developed as those in humans and so their experience of awareness must be more limited, but, given that they have the fundamental components of brain and body there must be some sense of consciousness. In fact their awareness seems better than ours in some respects.

most concerned with sensory organ responses and which more involved in thinking.[107]

The discussion so far assumes that, via the brain, one is fully aware and ready to receive such signals as the body presents, but what about when one is asleep – and asleep without dreaming? One is not then immediately aware of signals from the sensory organs, trying to register heartbeats or trying to achieve higher satisfaction. And yet one is still alive. Clearly, the sensory organs and the brain are still active, but it seems that there is some instruction from the brain that the sensation received must reach some threshold level before one is awakened.

If one is asleep and dreaming, the level of awareness is different yet again. I am not sure what dreaming is, but vaguely remember reading that it has been suggested that it relates to a reordering of information held in the brain.[108] But the main point for this discussion is that, in a dream, the brain seems to treat actions as if they are real, even if they seem surreal at times. One may, therefore, dream of having the same sensations as one has when awake[109] and so this is also part of awareness. One must recognise, however,

---

[107] It is known that signals from the sensory functions are interpreted within the *cerebral cortex* part of the brain which is the most recently evolved part of the brain. This cortex consists of several lobes which all have identifiable functions. The *frontal* lobe is critical for thinking and reasoning; the *occipital* lobe for vision and colour recognition; the *temporal* lobe for hearing emotions, touch, language; the parietal lobe for information processing pain sensation, speech; the two *insula* for reading the physiological state of the body and activating responses to that (e.g. triggering eating to satisfy hunger). Interest in the insula has expanded considerably in more recent years and neuroscientists believe, so I am told, that they are the centre of social emotion (e.g. lust, disgust, guilt, empathy, response to music). It is in differences in the insula that brings about different levels of intensity of these emotions between animals and humans, although, it would seem to me, that animals do express some degree of these emotions. Also none of these lobes are entirely separate, but are part of an integrated network and so there is some overlapping of function between the different lobes. It has also been reported recently by researchers at Turku University in Finland that they have identified a 'Super Network' (involving the thalamus, anterior and posterior cingulate cortexes and angular gyri) deep inside the brain which could control consciousness.

[108] One recalls the Freudian view that dreams contain messages relating to repressed thought which, if unearthed, can help overcome psychosis.

[109] One can also have sensations which one cannot have while awake. One may dream, as

that the brain, on occasion, tells the dreamer *within the dream* that he or she is only dreaming – this seems to happen in particular when the dream is about something threatening. On such occasions the dreamer may be awakened from his or her slumbers, sometimes with quite a shock. The brain seems to monitor potential dangers even in this rather different form of awareness.

The contrast between awareness when awake and when asleep suggests another feature of the phenomenon. Awareness is not just there or not there in binary form, but there are different intensities of awareness, and, indeed, of consciousness as a whole. In sitting in my study typing this text on my computer, I am very aware of what is on the screen. I am also quite aware of what is on my desk around me, a little less aware of what is in the room, especially behind me, and even less aware of what is occurring in the garden outside, but very aware that my wife is in the kitchen and may call me for dinner at any moment even though I have no visual link with her from my study. But to some extent I am aware of all these things at the same time and, if necessary my main attention can switch from one to the other very quickly to make me more aware of something other than the screen.

Thinking, Understanding and Reason

Being aware and having a knowledge base is not, however, thinking about it. I may become aware of something and immediately understand it without much thinking based on previous experience available in my memory bank. Even then some thought must go into defining the matter of which I have just become aware and the searching and matching that with similar records in my memory. Often, however, my memory will not provide an exact example of what is involved and then I may want to gain an understanding of what is involved. Note, even then, that I may decide that there is no

---

I have often done, that one is flying without wings through air above a village by using a swimming breaststroke type of action. Is this a genetic throwback in the brain to some prior ancestor that could fly or swim or is it a different aspect of being conscious being explored by the brain?

memory match, but I still do not want to bother to understand it. That also involves thinking. I may well, however, want to gain a better understanding and this will involve the use of reason. I may need to study the issue in more depth such as trying to grasp the methodology behind a mathematical solution or how the constituent parts of some physical structure fit together. Alternatively, I may seek out someone whom I think is more informed about my issue. Eventually, although for most aspects of my everyday living all this may take place almost instantaneously, I may want to take action. Then alternate options may be considered and a selection made. Clearly, thinking and reason is involved in all these processes. It also seems obvious that all these processes take place within the brain. But is not the brain a physical operating mechanism like other parts of the body? It seems, therefore, quite understandable that, historically, some philosophers have argued that a soul or Mind[110] must exist which is separable from the body and the brain. This soul/Mind is said to provide the will to act – or instructs the brain to provide the action signals.

Descartes[111] argued that there is a sharp distinction between the Mind and the body and it is the Mind that informs the body. In his view, the Mind encompasses not just awareness, but what reactions are possible and what action to take. The essence of Mind is, therefore, thinking and making decisions. If this 'Dualism' is an accurate tracing of human reality, the critical question arises of what is the form of the Mind, where is it located, and how does it communicate with the physical entity of the body? Or, was Descartes wrong and everything to do with the Mind is located in the brain? This is a key issue to be discussed.

The issue of whether everything is determined by neurons within the brain with no reference to an independent Mind was recently discussed by

---

[110] Sometimes it has even been argued to be a world spirit part of which sits in us as a soul. This now seems a very remote possibility, but it is not completely without some sense as discussed later in addressing the affect of the world on our Minds.

[111] See Kenny, op cit, Volume 3, pp 216–219.

Midgley[112] where she took issue with Crick.[113] Crick argued that something called a separate Mind simply did not exist. Midgley pointed out, rather forcefully, that Crick said

> ... your joys and your sorrows, your memories and your ambitions, your sense of personal identity and free will, are in fact no more than the behaviour of a vast assembly of nerve cells and their associated molecules.

Midgley said that this was now even the officially held message of science. How, Midgley argued, could this be acceptable? If there was not a thinking Mind, how did we get all this scientific knowledge? She continued that in Crick's world, where one gets rid of our memories, how could anyone think scientifically?

As I see it, she completely misinterpreted Crick. He does *not* say that we *get rid of* our memories, but that they are kept in our 'vast assembly of nerve cells'. He also is not saying that a Mind does not exist, but rather that it is not separate from the brain. Moreover, the quotation above given by Midgley was just the opening words of the Introduction to Crick's book which continues over about 300 pages to explore various aspects of consciousness. Later in his book, Crick says that while the genes appear to lay down the broad structure of the nervous system, experience is needed to tune up and refine many details of this structure and that *this is a continuing process throughout life*. The brain at birth is not fully equipped mentally. It has a structure derived through its genes, but needs experience to enable it to evolve to do an effective job. The mature brain is, therefore, the product of both Nature and Nurture at least during the length of one life. This notion is significantly expanded upon by Clark and Chalmers[114] to be examined in this Section shortly.

Returning to Nagel,[115] his reference to scientific method is similar to

---

112 M Midgley, op cit.

113 F Crick, *The Astonishing Hypothesis*, Simon & Schuster, 1994.

114 A Clark and D Chalmers, *The Extended Mind, in Philosophy of mind: Classical and contemporary readings*, ed. D Chalmers, Oxford University Press, 2002

115 T Nagel, *Mind and Cosmos*, op cit.

Midgley's. He extends his argument to recognise that the reductionist, materialistic approach to the development of physical science and biology has certainly made huge progress in the understanding of life and the universe. He is very sceptical, nevertheless, whether this reductionist approach can provide an adequate explanation of consciousness. He says science certainly cannot currently explain, at present, how life began,[116] why there was a need for conscious beings or how consciousness came into being. He makes clear throughout his book that he is sceptical as to whether a reductionist science can ever provide explanations for these matters.

When Nagel focuses on consciousness, he stresses that a sound theory of its development will necessitate a consideration of its place in the evolution of life including that of animals as well as humans and that current theories based on reductionism will need to be expanded to incorporate a broader approach to this enquiry.

It is clearly correct to see consciousness as a developing phenomenon as part of the evolution of life and to recognise that beings other than humans exhibit consciousness. One must, however, be very careful how one defines both life and consciousness when making such a statement. Dawkins shows how the whole of life, having existence now for about 4 billion years, consists of three major life groups[117] of which animals only comprise a small subsection of just one of those groups which also includes plants and fungi. Consciousness in some form arose in the earliest forms of life and throughout *all these three groups*. Early single cell organisms did not have brains or nervous systems, but they did have ways of sensing and responding to their environment. That might not be consciousness as usually conceived, but it suggests a precursor of the development of consciousness. Eventually, our ancestors populated the land, about 400 million years ago, and the first mammals came into existence about 200 million years ago. By then these living beings had developed brains and, in particular, mammals had extra

---

[116] Although various plausible suggestions have been made. See the discussion in R Dawkins, *The Ancestor's Tale*, op cit, Rendezvous 39.

[117] Archaea, Eubacteria and Eukarya (the last includes animals), Dawkins, *The Ancestor's Tale*, op cit.

layers of neural tissue on the surface of their brains which enabled more complex patterns of behaviour. Somewhat later Man appeared with even more sophisticated brains and, hence, an even more sophisticated sense of consciousness. His development of language also meant he made a huge leap ahead in his conscious ability compared to other mammals.

Nagel is, therefore, quite correct to say that there is a need to understand how consciousness developed and its place in the evolution of life, but I do not see that as fundamentally problematic. If one leaves aside the very outset of the formation of life, consciousness did not just suddenly come into existence. It has, almost certainly, evolved based upon genetic mutation from a very crude and basic sensing to the level humans experience today. Moreover, there is no mystery about why consciousness was needed. Improvements in consciousness enabled survival in a competitive world. It is also clear that there are different levels of consciousness enjoyed by different forms of life, from very basic organisms, to animals and humans. It is, however, just human consciousness that I am concerned with in this text. While, we may not yet have a detailed explanation of how this evolution occurred, it does not seem, in principle, to be a mystery of how consciousness evolved from a basic sensing mechanism.

I've already mentioned that Midgley does not see how consciousness can be explained by a reductionist, materialistic science and that Nagel[118] also adopts this view. He says that a teleological approach to understanding is needed to complement the reductionist view of the world.[119] I have argued earlier, however, that an array of purposive explanations are already available for even physical aspects of evolution. Moreover, when one moves from physical to social evolution, it is downright obvious that developments have been affected by human intention as will be discussed in Section 6. So a theory of all evolution, including both physical and social, must incorporate an understanding of how purpose has driven change as well as the Selfish Gene modified as appropriate by Genetic Drift and Recombination as described by Wagner. However, one must also now explicitly recognise that

---

[118] Nagel, op cit, chapters 3 and 4.

[119] Midgley and others have also advocated this view.

evolution includes the evolution of consciousness.

If Nagel and Midgley drop teleology as that needed to supplement Darwinian and Neo-Darwinian thought to explain evolution and, instead, accept straightforward individual intention and events as the supplementary influences, I agree with them, but there still remains the specific issue of whether the evolution of consciousness in particular can be explained by scientific means or by human intention. I feel that reductionist studies of the brain have a good chance of eventually explaining the part the brain plays in bringing about consciousness and reason,[120] although, as explained below, that may not be a full explanation of the Mind.

I argued earlier that one should not simply adopt agnosticism about the existence of God without pushing one's thinking further to ask what possible form of God could exist given our present knowledge. Similarly, we should not dismiss reductionist scientific methods for being incapable of explaining the processes in the brain without examining what scientific approaches are available and being explored. So what approaches does science offer?

Reference has already been made to Crick's views. His belief probably reflects much mainstream scientific thinking currently about the processes

---

[120] My view is that, adaptation may occur by random mutation of genes, but at all stages of evolution there was the intention of the viruses, bacteria, animals, indeed all forms of life, to survive. This is more obvious to us in the case of animals and humans seeking food and resisting attacks upon them. It is difficult to conceive of life existing at all without this desire; life does not continue by accident. The presence of such a desire does not come from the Darwinian Theory which merely explains those able to survive do so. So it is legitimate to ask where did these intentions come from? I suggest that most human intentions are the product of lived experience bar the intention to survive (and some preferences, such as taste for different foods, which probably come at least in part via the legacy of our genes). Our brains are like blank sheets at birth and we learn how to do things and develop preferences and dispositions, but the fundamental intention to survive is present from birth in all living creatures. It must have been, as argued by Nagel, introduced when life itself was created. That does not mean that it will never be explained in just physical terms. It may just be impossible to explain it with current physical knowledge. Nagel seems to think some other explanation than physicalism will eventually be found, but, as stated above, he does not know what it is and neither does anyone else. If there is another explanation not derivable from reductionist science, it must come from an examination of how intentions, especially that of survival, arise.

and structure of the brain. This suggests that if we were able to trace all connections in the brain's neural network and compute the output of the brain in different circumstances we might be able to show how humans will think and act in each of them. Some argue that, essentially, this is to say that scientists will be able to understand the operation of the brain in a way very similar to understanding complex printed circuits in computers as a computation system.

Crick does not totally dismiss this, but, in discussing neural networks, he emphasises the complexity of the system. Even the behaviour of a single neuron is far from simple. Neurons are connected together in complex ways and the whole system, he says, is highly non-linear. This makes neuron behaviour much more complex and makes prediction difficult and often results turn out to be counter-factual. He continues that the brain does not even look a little bit like a general purpose computer. Nevertheless, he then continues to describe a range of modern approaches based on Artificial Intelligence, Parallel Distributed Processing, Unsupervised Learning systems and other computerised neural networks. He concludes that these networks have achieved considerable performance and many new ideas are being developed. These developments may, primarily, lead to commercial benefit, but they *may* also lead to important results for thinking about the way the brain operates. One can at least glimpse, he says, the possibility that some day it will be possible to model the brain in a biologically realistic way.

Hence, there is already much in science that is devoted to exploring such a computational approach. There is, however, still good cause to wonder if such an approach can possibly yield an adequate explanation of the working of the brain. It was stated earlier that consciousness does not exhibit binary characteristics with on/off states. This might suggest that a computer with binary functioning is unlikely to replicate the brain. In addition, when one considers the scale of the problem in understanding neural networks as computational devices, it is very large indeed. There are about 100 billion neurons in a human brain. Even if quantum computing is developed further to overcome the binary nature of current computers, the problem will still be immense. In fact, the problem may be even more severe than just suggested. To see why, one needs to understand arguments by Penrose in what *The Times* described as one of the most important works of the second half of the 20th century.[121]

Penrose describes how single-celled paramecia currently exist with no nervous system or brain, but which can swim about in the pond, catching bacteria for food or retreating when danger lurks and yet they have no nervous system or brain. They do this by means of cilia, numerous hair-like legs, which exist on the outside of the cell's cytoskeleton (a structure that holds the cell together). This suggests that consciousness, at least in rudimentary form, cannot depend upon the existence of neurons. However, neurons are single cells with each having its own cytoskeleton which itself contains microtubules. It is these microtubules that, says Penrose, organise the strength of synapses and modifying their strength when needed. They are, hence, central to the operation of the brain.

I am hardly qualified to do more than report what I have read in Penrose, but he states the extra problem this brings to computer-like approaches. Quoting Moravec he says that, if one adopts a neuron-only active model of the brain, the human brain might achieve 1014 operations per second, whereas, if we consider the tubulin dimmer[122] as the basic computational unit, we would expect about 1027 operations per second. Modern computers can, I believe, get close to 1014, but will not achieve 1027 for the foreseeable future.

So from a quite different perspective, Penrose, like Nagel, Midgley and Crick, feels that consciousness is unlikely to be explained fully by computational means, but his reason is by no means confined to just

---

[121] R Penrose, *Shadows of the Mind*, Vintage Books, 1994, Chapter 7. Penrose received the Nobel Prize, jointly with Stephen Hawking. Crick also, in his well-known association with Watson, received the Nobel Prize for his discovery of DNA. So the views of such persons are not to be taken lightly. Penrose has also in recent years devoted much attention to the topic of consciousness. See also Penrose, Hameroff and Kak (editors), *Consciousness and The Universe*, Cosmology Science Publishers, 2017 and Penrose (with others), *The Large, The Small and the Human Mind*, Cambridge University Press, 1997.

[122] Apparently, microtubules consist of tubulin as subunits which in turn have dimmers as subunits which can have different geometric shapes according to their electric polarisation caused by movements of an electron. It is obvious why I say 'apparently' – I am just reporting what I have read!!

that it would be too complex. His reasoning is far more fundamental. He distinguishes between top-down and bottom-up modelling. Top-down models which comprise the vast majority of current computers have well-defined fixed computational procedures intended to provide definite solutions. Bottom-up models are designed to learn through different trial and error simulations with both procedures and the memory base modified through repeated runs. The bottom-up approach is what underlies developments in Artificial Intelligence. Penrose, however, believes that neither top-down nor bottom-up models can explain the workings on the human brain, specifically that human mathematical understanding is something quite different from computation and cannot be completely supplanted by it.

Chapter 3 of *Shadows of the Mind* takes almost 100 pages of various strands of thought to establish this position. It is not necessary to go into this detail here, but merely to note that this conclusion leads Penrose to look for a non-computational physics of the Mind which in turn will, in his view, require a completely new development in the understanding of physics itself. He then spent the second half of his book addressing the possible form of new physics that will be needed to understand the Mind from a scientific point of view. He concludes with the suggestion that it will probably be through the application of Quantum Theory that the workings of the brain will become known, but he does feel that, *eventually*, science will resolve this issue and, even, if he is wrong about that, attempts at a solution will provide much more insight. It should be stated that this revolutionary approach is not supported by many physicists. Yet, the fact that it is offered so seriously by someone of Penrose's stature, helps us consider the position of reductionist science versus views of some philosophers.[123]

The views of these scientists tend to support Nagel in at least saying that explaining the Mind completely by current reductionist methods may be extremely difficult. Nagel, however, offers a more fundamental reason

---

[123] It is would be interesting to know what Penrose's views are in relation to the proposed developments directly linking up computer chips with human brains as discussed briefly in Section 2.

in an earlier paper. His scepticism about a complete explanation coming from materialistic methods is not just due to the problem of complexity. He argues[124] that it is quite impossible for a person to know what the perception of a bat is like. We may be able to specify scientifically and precisely how a bat's body functions, but that it not the same as knowing what the bat perceives and feels. The Mind has feeling and this is unlikely to be understandable through current scientific method.

A similar argument is provided by the physicist Carroll[125] who refers to a proposal by Penrose and Hameroff. It has been stated that Penrose thought that a new approach to scientific enquiry is needed to understand consciousness which would probably involve Quantum Theory. Penrose and Hameroff attempt to develop a theory which relates the collapse in microtubules in the brain as an explanation of consciousness. Carroll suggests, however, that this approach using quantum processes to determine the rate at which neurones fire

is of no help whatever in bridging the gap between 'the firing of our neurones' and 'our subjective, self-aware experience'.

Carroll does go on to say, however, that although tiny changes in the rate of neurological processes are unlikely to be relevant in bridging the gap between the 'easy problem' of consciousness (understanding how the brain works) and the 'hard problem' (the subjective first-person experience), if they did, it would seem that this could be repeated in computers. He also says that many scientists, like himself, and philosophers believe that this gap will be bridgeable somehow.

Searle[126] makes a similar point in emphasising the difference between understanding how the brain operates and understanding what it is like to be oneself. With his 'Chinese Room Argument', he addresses the issue of whether any Artificial Intelligence (AI) computer could have

---

[124] T Nagel, What is it like to be a bat? In *The Philosophy of Mind,* op cit, ed. D Chalmers.

[125] S Carroll, op cit.

[126] JR Searle, *Mind – a brief introduction*, Oxford University Press, 2004 and originally in Minds, brains and programs, *Behavioural and Brain Sciences*, 1980.

consciousness. He rejects such a notion. He says that any computer has a control mechanism that implements a given programme, but it does not have an understanding of how that programme was written or the thinking behind it. The continuing difference between humans and computers will be that the former have this deeper understanding and consciousness. Even advanced AI machines will, he believes, never have consciousness.

However, this conclusion is not shared by everyone. Chalmers[127] concludes his book with

> The conclusion is that there do not appear to be any in-principle barriers to the ambitions of artificial intelligence ... we have good positive reason to believe that implementation of an appropriate computation will bring conscious experience along with it. So the outlook for machine consciousness is good in principle, if not yet in practice.

So the issue remains to be resolved in the future, although there seems to be agreement amongst most scientists (at least those who have studied consciousness) and most, but not all, philosophers, that consciousness will not be completely explained by conventional scientific method or likely computational methods (including quantum processes). New scientific approaches may eventually explain a lot more about the brain's role, but that is unlikely to explain completely what the consciousness of any individual is. On the other hand, as Carroll says, many do believe that this gap will be explained one day.

On the other hand, I feel that one must not push too far Nagel's observation, based on bats, about the impossibility of knowing exactly what another human brain is perceiving. He is obviously correct, social scientists involved in qualitative research have long known that different people will often have different recollections of similar events and feelings about them which can lead to problems in deciding what really occurred and what was really perceived. However, it is possible to narrow down the area of ambiguity. There are methods for attempting to assess the degree of agreement over perceptions. At the trivial level, most organisations evaluating

---

[127] DJ Chalmers, *The Conscious Mind*, Oxford University Press, 1996.

customers' satisfaction with consumer products use simple scoring systems whereby respondents are asked to provide a measure between 1 to 5 or 1 to 10 reflecting their like or dislike for the product. Such methods are also used in medicine to gauge pain levels or other medical conditions. So, at least between humans through the use of language, one can make a stab at assessing what different people feel and perceive. Of course, one can never be sure that person A thinks of a score of 5 as person B does and so the eventual assessment is only a broad indicator, but the fact that it is so widely used, suggests that such guides are useful and that one can, to some extent and at a practical level, compare perceptions and feelings. In addition, if one could not communicate some idea of such feelings, social life would be impossible. We may not want a social life with bats, but we do with humans and so we need to be able to make some reasonable assessment of others' feelings – it is called empathy.[128]

Before moving on, I want to re-emphasise a point made earlier. I have discussed awareness separately from thinking/reason, but, as stated at the outset of this Section, in operation they are often intertwined, especially when one is trying to understand something one has not met before. There must be an initial perception that there is something to be resolved: one is conscious of a situation, one then thinks about it, often not resolving the problem completely, but coming to understand more precisely the nature of the problem. For example, one might wish to discover how some mechanical device works in order to repair it, or how to approach the proof of a mathematical equation or even how to write this pamphlet. This initial thinking advances our consciousness or knowledge of the issue. Eventually, after perhaps many rounds in this process, one arrives at a solution or gives up searching for one. Either way, awareness and knowledge have evolved a little more. In this case, awareness is enhanced as a result of thinking (reason).

---

[128] Empathy is defined as understanding another's feelings, intentions or difficulties and that is how I want to use the term in this text. For reasons that will become clear later in this text, empathy needs to be kept distinct from sympathy although in everyday language the two often seem to be used interchangeably. One can be quite aware of another's perspective without being in sympathy with that person.

Consciousness in Context

After taking into account all that has been discussed in this Section, can any conclusion be made, and, in particular, about the views of philosophers like Nagel and Midgley? I think the answer is 'Yes'. In my view they were too extreme in their criticism of the reductionist materialistic approach to understanding consciousness as it was earlier argued they were with regard to the Selfish Gene Theory. They were, nevertheless, correct to question the likelihood of reductionist materialistic approaches ever leading to a *complete* understanding of consciousness. Both Crick and Penrose say that science may well eventually work this out, but both emphasise the severe problems to be overcome in doing so. There is, more fundamentally, the question of the need to understand what other factors might need to be understood that are not amenable to reductionist enquiry, if the latter does not prove to be up to the task. It will be necessary to understand how such factors are initiated and how and how they interact with processes in the brain.

In commenting on Huxley, Midgley, like Nagel, states that the brain and the Mind are not isolated from each other, but must be considered in a social and evolutionary context. This can have two different interpretations. The first involves considering how the brain evolved since life began and, as has been discussed above, one can point to some role of intentions in this process. The second interpretation relates to how some philosophers feel that the Mind is a social phenomenon as well as a biological and neurological one. This is why, presumably, they argue for the teleological factor to be incorporated into our consideration of consciousness. But, if the operation of consciousness occurs *wholly* through the neurons of the brain which now seems clear that it must, how can social and environmental factors (not teleological factors) influence a brain that we inherit based on our genes? Midgley's and Nagel's call for attention to the social context seem to be largely based on intuition[129] and expressed as though it is obvious. Also I admit to feeling intuitively that they must be correct. We need, however, to

---

[129] At least as expressed in their two books that I have cited, though they might well have developed their arguments further elsewhere.

move beyond intuition.

First, it is obvious that as a person accumulates experience, much of it will go into his memory bank of awareness and be taken into account in reasoning and deciding on actions. There may be, however, be a more fundamental way in which experience and social factors help to adapt the actual processes in the brain that produce consciousness. How might this occur? The answer possibly lies in Crick's observation, noted earlier, that the genes only provide the newborn with a brain structure that is not fully mature and that, *throughout our lifetimes*, the brain evolves in response to environmental pressures and experiences. Wagner[130] reiterates the point:

> Preparing the Mind requires a life's worth of learning and experiences. These experiences lay down a pattern of neural wiring that guides which new thoughts, images, or melodies can emerge spontaneously.

Certainly, it is known that the size of boys brains reach a maximum at about 14 or 15 and that the most rapid growth occurs before about six years of age, but the brain continues to mature beyond that with neurons getting bigger, working more effectively and adjusting trillions of connections as a result of *external stimuli*. Some point out the frontal lobes that are involved in planning, memory and control of reaction mature at about the mid-thirties, but others stress that much depends upon the individual and the context within which he or she lives. One scientist (Reiss of Stanford University) says some maturation and refinement of neural networks and coordination can continue until 82![131]

At once we have an understanding of how social factors, as well as the biological ones, influence the development of different *physical* parts of the brain as we mature.[132] This raises the question of whether even the operation

---

[130] Wagner, op cit, p 146.

[131] Reading this made my day, now nearing 82! But if this is right, why should it stop before death?

[132] It is said that some people have a greater musical ability, located in different parts of their brains, through their genetic heritage. This, however, lies fairly dormant unless the person self-trains or is trained to develop this ability and make it operational. Hence, true intentions occur in developing that musical consciousness. The same must be true of

of our neural networks themselves may be modified due to our experiences. There is an interaction between the social and the physical operations in the brain, not just in the way the brain absorbs social information and assesses it, *but in the way the brain physically works.* The total operating system we call the Mind is then a *combination* of the social with the biological and neurological. If one accepts this view, it is also clear that the individual's Mind is not just affected by his direct experiences, but that it is also a product of much broader social factors which impinge upon his life and act to form his or her identity as discussed below. Then one can consider a much broader social pressure working to inform individual consciousness. Nagel is very tentative in stating what this broader pressure might be, but he states:

> ... the consciousness, the knowledge, and the choice, are dispersed over a vast crowd of beings, acting both individually and collectively.

It is there that he has the kernel of how factors not subject to reductionist research do affect the brain and, hence, consciousness. He had no need to continue to say:

> These teleological speculations are offered merely as possibilities, without positive conviction.

He had, in my view, already arrived at the correct conclusion, but the explanation is not some teleological law but just a recognition of how the world probably works.

The idea that the Mind, and its underlying neurological foundations, is influenced by a range of experiences and information outside of location in the brain has been exhaustively argued by Clark and Chalmers as indicated

---

development in the brain to master language or, indeed, any mental skill. It is then logical to extend this experiential and environmental influence on the *physical* operation of the brain to all experiences. Moreover, if experiences can lead to the development of different parts of the brain and comparative sizes according to experience, can the same happen to the basic processes by which neurons operate within those sectors? Will not an advanced mathematician have his/her neurons functioning to some extent in a way different to mine? I think it is likely!

earlier. Clark[133] then extended his analysis considerably. He argues that the boundary of the Mind should not be considered to be the human skull, but to encompass a whole range of external influences. He says that, if we eventually transplant a computer into human brains to, say, enhance our memory or calculating ability, will that not become part of the Mind? If so, what is the difference between that computer and one to which we have ready access outside of our body?

Clark extends his argument then to refer to all sorts of information which may actively impinge upon the operation of our consciousness and the Mind. It is very clear that a wide range of external information influences our perceptions and often leads to beliefs and dispositions that in turn influences behaviour. Recognition of such a point could simply be taken to infer that the internal Mind absorbs rather passive information and acts upon it as necessary. However, Clark goes far beyond this and develops the idea of the Extended Mind incorporating *both* our internal Mind and external information that is often in *active interaction* with our internal brain processes.

What sense should be assigned to the phrase 'being active' in such a context? Usually being active implies something is alive. Hence, external influences can be divided into two categories; those that are alive and those that are inanimate. It is obvious that our own Minds are influenced actively by other people with Minds of their own. Our dispositions and beliefs in fields such as religion, belief in God, politics, ethics and all sorts of human behaviour are affected by the view of others. It is also obvious that the state of others affects feelings of sympathy. But does that justify a definition that includes all Minds of others as part of *my own* Mind? Certainly, there is usage of the everyday phrase 'of being of one mind' when agreement is reached and also the phrase 'meeting of the minds'. I would prefer the latter rather than attempting to define my Mind as *encompassing* many other influences from other Minds. Moreover, it is obvious that there is a mass of inanimate information that influences our behaviour. (Much of it, though not all, is produced by people with alive minds.)

---

[133] A Clark, *Supersizing the Mind*, Oxford University Press, 2011.

Do we want to define our Mind as including all this information? If we follow this line of thought, at the limit could we not argue that our behaviour is to some extent influenced by all, or nearly all, physical and mental information about the whole world and there is only one Mind? That, however, would be extending the argument to absurdity and, of course, Clark does not do that. It would ignore the fact that different people have different feelings, dispositions, intentions, etc., and so it only makes sense to talk of individuals having their own Mind even if each one is hewed out of physical and social interaction.

While I can see that one could define each Mind as incorporating much that is social, what purpose does that serve? It seems to me that Clark has made an extremely useful contribution in emphasising how we cannot understand the operation of the human Mind without considering all links with outside active and dynamic influences arising beyond our skulls. But I prefer to think of each of us having our own different Mind which is the product of physical events/information and other peoples' Minds, interacting with our own unique neurological system. As mentioned earlier, Crick pointed out that babies are born with underdeveloped brains which gradually mature as they learn about their world. It was also suggested earlier that this development can continue until old age, although most of it occurs in the earlier stages of life. I suggest that this is totally in keeping with Clark's ideas. As humans learn they adopt knowledge, beliefs, definitions and dispositions that get stored in their brains. Most of his information obviously must come from sources beyond the brain. (I say 'most' because, as the person matures, he or she may have their own internally generated original ideas coming from their own manipulation of this information which is then stored in their memory.) This internally held information will then be the basis of unconscious responses or further thought. Then, as Crick suggests, the process of learning and storing information in memory will impact upon the neurons in the brain. Hence, there can be little question that Clark is correct to emphasise the interrelationship between a person's Mind and his environment. Moreover, as learning and Mind adaptation takes place through life, in most people it probably lessens in pace as our beliefs, dispositions and information necessary for living and careers are assimilated and become more fixed, with new learning tailing off as we mature. Even then, however, external influences can shake up our dispositions where personal crises occur, such as major illness, political or social revolutions, or major crises arising from the natural world or even just curiosity. Also, of course, neurons still function so long as humans are thinking. If, as I very tentatively suggest, there is a lessening of pace of learning, it is just a matter of degree to which neuron activity does slow down. None of this, however, seems to justify treating a human Mind as the Extended Mind and sum of both internal and external influences. The core influence is still the internal Mind. Clark himself does recognise this, but seems to prefer the much wider definition of Mind. I recognise all that Clark says, but prefer to define the Mind as within our skulls influenced by many factors outside it.

In closing this subsection, it seems appropriate to recall Descartes' Dualism. It now seems generally agreed that he was wrong to suggest that a Mind existed separately outside of the body.[134] Also, quite recently, Midgley[135] has argued that, with modern hindsight, it is clear that Descartes was in error in proposing a Dualism and that Mind and matter are all part of the same reality. If Dualism occurs, the separation *occurs wholly within my brain* and not part within it and part outside of it. Certainly, it does seem logical for there to be a duality with part of the brain instructing other parts, even though the operation of the brain is partly influenced by matters external to the body.

In contrast some, for example, Ryle[136] argued that the traditional understanding of consciousness depended upon an improper Cartesian duality which distinguished between Mind and body. For him,

---

[134] Kenny, op cit, Volume 4, pp 212–219 explains how Wittgenstein undermined the notion of 'Dualism' while also avoiding an adoption of the behaviourist view (which hitherto had provided the main criticism of 'Dualism') that one had to explain thought or consciousness from studying behaviour. He could not see how a totally psychical mind could exist, but, in addition, the behaviourist approach was invalid because one could never measure the thought or consciousness of another individual. Also see Searle in Magee, op cit, p 345.

[135] M Midgley, *What is philosophy for?*, Bloomsbury Academic, 2018.

[136] G Ryle, *The Concept of the Mind*, University of Chicago Press, 1949.

consciousness could not be separated from our complete behaviour and linguistic understandings. That may be so, but that does not completely undermine Dualism in a slightly different sense. It does not invalidate the notion of Dualism within my brain. It is quite possible that part of my brain receives a continual stream of consciousness both directly and from sensations elsewhere in my body, but, following thinking, instructions are then given by a separate part of the brain telling one how to act.

Despite this, Searle[137] and Clark[138] argue against any form of duality. Both envisage an ongoing, dynamic process whereby neurons jostle with memory, intentions and influences from which emerges a decision to act. Searle says that the neurons are not conscious, but they form a part of the brain that is conscious. He also says that the neurons are lower level operators which give rise to the higher level biological processes of consciousness. He does not say, however, how this occurs. Indeed, it is not yet known. Clark also seems to go along with this view. In responding to a critic he says that he accepts the idea of a

> biological memory (being) such an active process as to blur the distinction between memory systems and reasoning system.

To conclude on duality, it would seem that it either exists within the brain or that it does not exist at all. I cannot see any definite evidence yet to establish which is correct. It does seem clear, nevertheless, that our Mind is a biological, rather than just a neural, function. As Nagel said, reported earlier in this text, we may come to understand through science exactly how neurons work in the bat's brain, but we can never *know* what it is like to be a bat. The reason must be because we are biologically different. We can never know what it is like to fly around guided by sonar signals or sleep hanging upside down in a cave exactly as bats do. Moreover, even two members of the same species can never know precisely what it is like to be each other. This again is because they are not biologically identical. They may have

---

[137] JR Searle, *Mind – a brief introduction*, op cit. Indeed, practically his whole book is devoted to attacking the notion of duality.

[138] A Clark, *Supersizing the Mind*, op cit.

very similar experiences and understanding, especially of body sensations, but, even then, it is well known that, for example, people have different pain thresholds and differ in the way they get side effects from taking the same drug. Even more fundamentally, each of us has different experiences which I am told do have an impact on the way our individual neural systems operate.

I cannot but agree, therefore, that Searle and Nagel are both correct in saying that understanding the Mind must be made at a biological level. This also implies that the very impressive work by scientists like Penrose and Crick (also reported earlier) may well lead eventually to a detailed knowledge of how the brain and its neural network functions, but it cannot provide one being with exact knowledge of what it is like to be another. This surely also applies to any future development in Artificial Intelligence or robotics. Using the following phrase in rather a different sense to its normal usage – 'I know my own Mind' and no one else can *really* know it.

Free Will [139]

The discussion above has addressed amongst other things the inter-relationship between consciousness and human intention. This is not quite the same point as asking whether a human actually has free choice in making decisions. Obviously, no one has a completely free choice as there are always social and physical constraints to behaviour that cannot be simply wished away. But the debate about free will goes much deeper than this. This is a subject that almost every leading philosopher over the last 2,000 years has addressed at some time. Plato and Aristotle addressed this in different ways, but thereafter, Christianity (and other religions) debated the topic from a theological viewpoint. The crux of that debate was how Man could have free will when there was an omniscient God? If free will occurred, it could only have been if God allowed it. Man could then choose between good and evil and, eventually after death, be accountable for it.

---

[139] It is interesting that Crick adds a postscript on free will to his book. In that postscript he says that he thinks he can identify where, in the brain, the will resides.

Even if God is left out of the picture, there are still, in the 21st century, some arguing against free will. This seems to be based on the argument that, if all physics is deterministic (that is to say, given an accurate specification of an initial position, physics-based rules will determine the outcome) and humans are just as much subject to the rules of physics as anything else, how can our actions not be fully caused by the situation we find ourselves in? It would also follow that if we can trace exactly how the brains works through its neural network to make a decision, what we will do in response to each stimulus will be computable and completely predictable. The literature on this subject is massive. I am not familiar with 99 per cent of it and, hence, cannot provide a summary here, but I can offer what occurs to me that free will is.

Even if Man does eventually manage to trace how the brain with its neural network operates physically when thinking, that does not necessarily mean that the result of that thinking process will be predictable. A crude analogy is that of a random number generator. We know how it works, but cannot predict its output except probabilistically. I do not think that the brain operates completely randomly, but there is uncertainty in the process. In outline, I suspect that the human brain first is aware of something, it then has to decide how to categorise it to deposit in the memory bank. This in itself might well be complex given the scale and scope of human memory. It will then decide whether action is needed and what action to take. It probably does this by examining its memory for similar situations or common features. Again I suspect that the data bank of possible actions is enormous if one considers all variations. Alternatively, the memory bank may offer no previous experience of a situation like that currently faced. Based on either remembered experiences or new innovative thinking, the brain then offers various options.[140] Moreover, the whole process probably

---

[140] Note that it seems to me that this sequence of events must occur whether the whole process takes place within a unified set of neurons as Searle and Clark propose or whether there is a form of duality within the brain with some of the neurons constituting the decision/control part and another set of neurons receiving the initial stimuli and holding the memory. The time gap between the initial stimulus and the decision must exist, even if it is infinitesimally short.

operates on a probabilistic rather than deterministic basis. Recall, also, the comments by Crick and Penrose above relating to the complexity of the human brain and the probable inability of computational methods to demonstrate how the brain works. Taking all this into account, I believe that we should not be concerned that the human will be robotised with all actions certain. There are probably many alternate paths through the brain to arrive at a solution that will, more often than not, simply produce a 'good enough' outcome, rather than optimal one looking at all possibilities. We may need to accept such a solution quickly in order to act in time. At times we may even want to persist and view a greater range of options than we do at other times, but there may be a cost of spending too much time on decision-making.

It follows that predicting an exact decision that an individual will make in any situation may be subject to considerable uncertainty. We may be able to predict accurately for some matters, especially where dispositions have become embedded, but not for most. Even if we come to know exactly how all the neurons and synapses operate, there will still be a thinking taking place in the brain that will result in habitual socially derived action, but also unpredictable outcomes in other situations. If one follows Penrose, even the probability of most outcomes will not be computable. The key point, then, is that even a complete physical knowledge of how the brain operates, does not have to imply that it prohibits human choice or make us less human. Nor will it make us completely predictable. Furthermore, I find it difficult to see how innovation, a continuing occurrence throughout all of social, physical and biological evolution, can take place at all without free will. Are we to say that all innovation is precisely predetermined and predictable? One could argue that innovations are 'caused' by crises and the unavoidable need for change, but the detail of each innovation and how they enable reaction to each crisis surely depends upon freedom of thought by human beings.

Searle[141] examines the topic of free will in depth. In doing so he describes the view of compatibilists who argue that to say that an action portrays

---

[141] JR Searle, op cit.

free will is not to say that it does not have antecedent causes. In the case of human decision-making they say the antecedent causes are the being's inner convictions and processes. Searle also says that most philosophers[142] today probably accept some variant of this view and he points to a rich heritage of the idea ranging from Hobbes, to Hume and up to Ayer. Searle, however, rejects this suggestion, particularly because we all have direct knowledge of our own capacity to undertake decision freely (within constraints as mentioned earlier). Despite the eminence of many of these compatibilists, it seems to me that their argument is very contrived. Of course our actions are caused by our convictions and brain processes. That does not address the question of whether or not, given these 'causes', we can do as we please. I believe that Man can exercise free will through a thinking process as suggested above.

Identity[143]

A key part of one's consciousness is an awareness of one's own identity (self-awareness) and this is a major factor in explaining one's behaviour. But how does one think about one's own identity, does one appraise it and to what extent can one change it?

It is quite clear that each of us does not have a fixed identity throughout our lives. Not only are we constantly changing physically, but also we are exposed to different stimuli, environments and learning. Despite such change, we each have a sense of continuing identity throughout our life. Perhaps the best way to start addressing this is to examine what we cannot be, rather than what we are. This then sets the limits to identity. There seem to be four main factors which limit what we can be at any one point of our lives. Genetic make-up, our legacy of birth and family, the experiences and

---

[142] If Searle is right, Nagel, like Searle, is an exception.

[143] The discussion of identity here needs to be distinguished very clearly from Searle's discussion of 'identity theory' which replaced behaviourism. (See *Mind – a brief introduction*, Oxford University Press, 2004) I am only concerned with identity as self-awareness and, occasionally, awareness of what someone else is.

learning we acquire and the general environmental context in which we find ourselves at any time.

The influence of genetic make-up on our identity is obvious. There is no way that I can be a six foot ten inches tall basketball player. I am just not built that way and there is nothing I can do about it. We all have 'God-given' potential through our genes, but that potential is not unlimited. Each of us will have different upper limits in ability to developing this potential. Some will have a natural tendency to play sport, some will have a more artistic temperament, some will be able to sing beautifully, some will have a strong mathematical ability and some may be accomplished in all these things, but humans usually inherit through their genes varying intensities of natural ability in different areas of physical and mental accomplishment. Of course, performance in all these areas may be improved by training, but, if the basic genetic material is not there in any one individual, the benefits to be derived from training will be limited.

Next, we each have a legacy at birth which continues to some extent through our family background. We may be able to cast off limits due to birth or upbringing in the process of growing up and becoming adult, but it is certain that we all start off from different starting points in life – some not much different and some considerably different. Hence, at the very least, in our early life what we think of as our identity will be largely influenced by this background. At least the initial direction of the path we are to take through life will be strongly influenced by this legacy and some of it may never be cast off. Part of our personal philosophies, beliefs and dispositions will be determined by birth and childhood, though we may be able to cast them off later.

Third, and perhaps the most important factor in determining identity as an adult, is the learning and experiences we have had. There is no way that I can now be a professional microbiologist – or professional philosopher! I have not had the necessary training and education and it is too late to acquire it now. Also the learning we do acquire, plus our exposure to art, ethical behaviour, poverty, wealth, religion, friends, work, indeed everything we have experienced, will act partly as a limit on what we can be, but will also be a dominant factor in shaping what we think we are.

Fourth, is the state of the external environment, not just the past environments in which we have lived, which has, as just stated, influenced our development, but the environment at the time one is considering what one's identity is. A person may have grown accustomed to exhibiting particular values, say, in relation to ethical behaviour or religion or lifestyle, but then find himself/herself confronted with war or economic boom or slump or be located in an entirely different religious or political community and feel obliged to modify behaviour. While one might say this is simply an extension of Factor 3 (experience and learning), it seems important in addressing what identity one thinks one has *now* to consider the current environment. One might think of oneself as wealthy, and then the stock-market collapses.

The factors just discussed will determine what one feels one's own identity is. This will probably be thought of in terms of a combination of one's own perception of athletic, intellectual, ethical, aesthetic, religious, social, political, national, regional and other abilities or dispositions. These will change over time, but transitions from one state to the next will, usually, amount to relatively small modifications[144] and it is the remaining continuity that provides the core of one's identity. Awareness and memory would seem to play a significant part in helping an individual see this continuity and hence core identity.

It is important too, to recognise that different individuals with whom one has or has had contact will differ in how they perceive my identity. This may be because they have had contact with me in different contexts. Colleagues I had when working as an academic will see me differently than friends at my golf club who, in turn, will see me differently than members of my family. They will have different sets of knowledge about me. Alternatively, their views about me may differ because they interpret the same behaviour that I have exhibited in different ways. I will also, to some extent, have a different perception of my own identity than any of these groups, but the perceptions of these 'others' may well be fed back, intentionally or incidentally, to cause me to modify behaviour and thence identity. Recall Clark's discussion of the

---

[144] An obvious exception would be a radical conversion to a religion or political party.

Extended Mind.

It also seems clear that one can build up a fairly comprehensive view of another person's identity by studying his/her behaviour. One can never, however, define that identity without question because that study of behaviour can never encompass the sum total of that individual's behaviour. An individual himself or herself may also associate his or her own identity with behaviour that has been externally observed. A person may feel, however, that he/she has a skill or thoughts about certain basic values that have never been publicised in observable behaviour. They may have experienced behaviour that has been kept private, but which that person still feels is part of their identity. To that extent the individual's own assessment of identity will be at variance from that observed by others – there is a difference between public and private persona. I conclude that one has both a private and (probably several) publicly perceived identities. To have a complete picture, one needs to understand both empirical behaviour and individual introspection. In the latter, the higher satisfactions as discussed earlier play a key role in forming an understanding of one's own internally perceived identity.

It should also be noted that our identity is multilayered and varies according to the role one is playing at any time. What we identify with helps to describe our identity. If one is, for example, playing rugby for a club in the West Country, one identifies with that club and region and competes with players in other clubs. If one is selected to play for one's country, one identifies with the country and perhaps collaborates with the rivals one contested at club level. The same happens in all aspects of life. Not only do other people have varying views on what our identity is, but we ourselves also adopt different aspects of identity as we pursue different activities.

To sum up, there is no such thing as a complete and fixed definition of one's identity throughout life. Personal identity, fairly obviously, changes over time. The individual will also focus on different aspects of his identity according to context. There will also be variations in the public perceptions of identity at any time according to who is doing the assessment. On the other hand, there will be aspects of identity that will continue throughout life. These might be considered to be the dominant characteristics of identity around which much variation occurs over time and context. It is clear that both one's internal and public identity are determinants and reflections of one's behaviour. Consideration of identity is therefore central to understanding human behaviour.

The notion of identity and its link with behaviour also applies to groups of broader associations whether they are clubs, ethnic groups, companies, public bodies, political parties, nation states or international organisations. As well as their own personal identity, members of all of these bodies will have a sense of organisational identity[145] – namely, this is what the group or organisation is and does. Obviously that influences behaviour of those entities and those within them. Indeed such organisational identities may override the identity an individual perceives that he has. To belong to the organisation, or if people are forced to be members, it may be necessary to act according to that organisation's declared identity and values even if it is contrary to their own. On occasion, other groupings or society in general may deem that group identity and its behaviour to be undesirable.[146] For those wanting change, it will then be necessary to challenge that group identity and encourage its members to follow their own. This emphasises that knowledge of identity is a central consideration in understanding of *all* individuals and organisations and must be recognised in discussion of some issues later in this text.

As a final point, there is quite different way of looking at identity. I have discussed previously the immense size of the universe and the very small amount of time the human race has spent in it.[147] From that perspective

---

[145] The organisational identity will also be multilayered and varying over time as applies to individual identities, but perception of identity at any one time and situation will help to explain behaviour.

[146] For example, Nazi Germany or extreme religious and racial groups (both white and black).

[147] When we consider how we see ourselves, there is also the question of whether there are other humans, or some other form of intelligent life, elsewhere in the universe (or multi-universes). On a probabilistic basis and recognising that the Earth is such a 'small dot' in the universe, it seems likely that we on Earth are not unique. On the other hand, we may be unique as we have no evidence yet to the contrary, although recent discoveries of planets of

our identity seems to indicate that we are puny beings, with a very short lifespan, and whatever identity we exhibit during our lives is not of very great consequence in the life of the universe. While recognising this, it is still pretty important to us while we live – it is almost certainly the only experience of life we shall have. Recognising this, it makes sense for each of us to maximise our benefits from being alive. Ionesco's play[148] contains a section where the general factotum is complaining about many features of life. The king responds to each, pointing out the positive side of each situation mentioned. He even points out the delight of eating a casserole and especially the simple carrot. By focusing more on all the basic and higher satisfactions that we get out of our human experiences, rather than the downside or even just taking them as given, we have a better chance of coming to know how wonderful it is to be given the chance to live consciously with the identity that we have.

---

other suns suggest that at least the Earth itself may not be unique in providing a basis for life. Our current knowledge is such that no sensible decision can yet be taken on this matter. On the other hand, viewed in quite a different way, current Man is not unique. It is clear from our present knowledge of biological evolution, anthropology and archaeology, that Man is merely the current product in a very long evolutionary chain. His current form of existence is not unique and he is most certainly an unfinished product!

[148] Eugène Ionesco, *Exit the King*, a play premiered in 1962.

Appendix 1
Development of the Human Brain

Much of the discussion in this Section has concerned the function of the human brain. While it is not needed for the argument in these notes, it is interesting to consider a recent argument of how the human brain has developed. A recent book (C Gamble, J Gowlett and R Dunbar, *Thinking Big*, Thames & Hudson, 2014) is part of the output of The British Academy's flagship project to celebrate the centenary of its foundation. The thesis of the book, based on research by two archaeologists and an evolutionary psychologist and their body of postgraduate researchers, addresses the question of how the human brain developed to distinguish us from other animals. It concludes that it was the development of our social lives which drove the growth of the human brain.[149] The human brain has tripled in size over the last 7 million years or so, but most of this growth has occurred in the last 2 million years, such that human brain size is about three times bigger than those of our closest relatives in the animal kingdom – the chimpanzees.

Gowlett et al. provide archaeological evidence that the size of human communities increased markedly from about 2 million years ago. As indicated just above, a steady increase in brain size also took place from about 2 million years ago, although the brains belonged to our *homo erectus* ancestors as neither *Neanderthals* nor *Homo Sapiens* (modern humans) had developed as separate species at that time. Maximum brain size amongst the homo genus occurred with the *Neanderthals*. Brain size of *Homo Sapiens* was slightly smaller, but the Neanderthals did have a larger body weight to handle. It is not absolute size of the whole brain that is significant in explaining our human mental capacities because much of our brain is concerned with the need for physical operation of bodily muscles: large

---

[149] In contrast, some recent Israeli research has argued that it was the demise of large mammals and the need to hunt much smaller agile ones that led to larger human brains.

bodies require more brain power. Elephants, for example, have brains four times larger than ours. It is the size of the cortex which is significant in explaining the ability to think and operate as modern humans do. Brian size has actually shrunk a little over the last 100,000 years, but then rebounded a little as it is thought better nutrition led to a decline in disease.

There have been a variety of competing hypotheses as to why this increase in brain size occurred, but the social competition argument seems to be the dominant one. Gowlett et al. show a very strong *association* between the development of critical brain size and the need to accommodate cultural, linguistic and technological needs. They do urge caution as the evidence is based on scant fossil data, but such evidence that exists persuades them that increasing social networks led to increasing brain size.

The book is very valuable at showing the association of the development of brain size and social evolution, but it does not get to grips with the *mechanism* by which this occurred. One can see that, following a Darwinian and post-Darwinian view of evolution (together with Recombination) and a process of natural selection, those with larger brains were more suited to surviving within the more developed social contexts, but what originally led to larger social networks and what made them evolve? A developing social network was not a natural event like an Ice Age; it came about through human intention. Hence, was it not the genetic variation leading to larger brain (cortex) size that enabled *Neanderthals* and *Homo Sapiens* to be develop social networks and thereby reap the cultural, economic, linguistic and other benefits which, in turn, may well have led to further increased brain size? It seems most likely that there was both a proactive (intentional) initial causation and growth of social networking and a reactive (natural selection) response.

It may be possible, nevertheless, that no process of natural selection was needed. If, once initiated by some increase in brain size, social development led to greater stimulation of the brain, could that directly have led to further increased brain size? This would be quite in keeping with the earlier discussion that the Mind is affected by environmental factors and this might include an expansion in brain size. We begin life with small brains and they grow to maximum size in about our fourth decade. As each generation experienced increased stimulation, perhaps that led to our brains growing larger *within each generation.*

Alternatively, better social organisation may have led to better nutrition which in turn led each succeeding generation to have better brain development. This may not be so surprising, because it is clear that improved nutrition has led, in general, to increasing overall body size over the last, say, 2,000 years (and, indeed, over much shorter lapses of time). But there is still a question to be asked. Most human brain size increase occurred from a time about 2 million years ago up to about 100,000 years ago. Surely development, mental stimulation and better nutrition has improved in leaps and bounds since BC 98,000 and so, if that were the mechanism for increasing brain size, why have our human brains not developed *in size* much more since then? Alternatively, is it appropriate to argue that as we get more technology at our fingertips and we have less need for internal memory or internal problem-solving skills, our brain size will decline again, leaving our Minds more dependent on information computer chips situated outside of our physical being?

Perhaps one should welcome the impressive and far-reaching research by Gowlett et al., while realising that there is still much further enquiry to undertake before a complete understanding of the increase in human brain size is available.

5.

Ethics

Ethics concerns values used to inform moral human action. It relates to the right or wrong nature of such action and the goodness or badness of motives behind the action. I concluded earlier that competition was central to life at all levels and this may be taken to imply that each must seek to win or, at least, not to lose. This needs to be interpreted with care. Outright competition may be eschewed for ethical reasons. However, competition may be modified for reasons having nothing to do with ethics. There may be different strategies adopted to win which do not depend upon just taking action as an individual or individual group or individual country. There may also be costs associated with different forms of competition such that a balance is needed between these costs and the degree of competition employed. For example, it is well-known from economics that oligopolies may modify their competitive instincts recognising what a rival might do. In addition, it may pay some parties to form liaisons in order to compete more effectively against a common opponent. Hence, in some instances, collaboration may go hand in hand with competition. This will be addressed below, but first let me address what I think occurs to many people when talking about ethics.

Fairness

I suspect that most people when questioned about ethics will find it easier to think first of everyday examples of non-ethical behaviour. I also suspect that many would think first about what is fair and that one should not take an unfair advantage over others due to a privileged position or cheating. There are much more fundamental unethical practices, such as murder or theft, which are considered so serious as to need society's legal system to exercise constraint, but I think that most people would take that as an absolute given with no discretion allowed.[150] They probably think about ethical behaviour where an individual has the choice, probably concealed from view, to act well or not, and this will involve a consideration of fraudulent practice and cheating. In some cases these acts will be subject to law and in others not.

Examples of cheating abound almost daily in the newspapers in all areas of life. Such unethical practices, with varying degrees of seriousness, include bankers manipulating exchange rates, rigging LIBOR, misleading customers with protection insurance deals, companies offering bribes to prominent individuals to get business, some taking fraudulent advantage of Government financial grants and subsidies, those with inside knowledge using this to profit on the stock exchange, footballers diving, claiming to have been fouled, and thence gaining free kicks, queue jumping or anyone telling lies to maintain some sort of personal advantage – one could continue to list many examples of possible unethical practice in most forms of human activity.[151] It seems pretty clear that these types of actions are clearly unethical and morally wrong even though they may also be seen by the perpetrators as competing effectively for resources. As a consequence some more serious forms of cheating are actually classified as crimes and subject to punishment or, in the case of football, against the rules of the game and so punishable within the game. At this level of description, with these examples taken without context, it seems to me that there is not much of a philosophical issue. However, philosophical issues arise when some of these actions are considered within context.

The person cheating may well claim that many involved in an activity act unethically so that it is an unfair game in which he or she cannot hope to succeed if not also cheating. If footballers on one side are known to dive to win penalties, then one way of making the contest fair is for the other side also to cheat. Similarly, if it is established business in one part of the world

---

[150] Of course, some in society will think nothing of committing murder or theft, which is why the laws must be in place, but, mercifully, such people are few.

[151] A very current concern with the move to more online university teaching and examination due to the coronavirus crisis is the possibility for increased cheating.

to give 'backhanders' to gain business, the company that does not may always lose out when bidding for contracts in that locality. So there is always the call for 'a level playing field'. But, if one accepts that cheating on both sides should be allowed to make the game fair, one has effectively accepted that the game is different from its initial design – the best at cheating wins or at least strengthens their position. If one does not want to change the nature of the game in that way, one has to insist that *all* cheating is unethical whatever the consequences and an appropriate form of policing/refereeing the game needs to be devised with associated penalties for breaches of the ethical code. In my view, in such clear circumstances as those above, it is wise to keep to the original game without cheating or one risks getting on to a slippery slope with no clear view as to where the modification of the game may end, but one can observe, especially in sport, officials who allow some margin in interpreting what is cheating (e.g. not putting the ball in straight in a rugby scrum[152]) presumably in the wider interests of keeping the game moving. Similarly, flexibility at the margin must occur in deciding whether to take action on other forms of cheating.

In many walks of life, however, individuals may be relied upon to act ethically without policing; religion has historically had a large part to play in conditioning such human behaviour.[153] If religions experience more widespread lack of observance, there is the danger of leaving a void within which there is no clear social code of ethical practice. In contrast, Paine[154] argued that he believed there is some form of God because we all have an innate sense of moral value which would seem to imply that we do not need formal religions to guide our behaviour. But, given my earlier positioning on the existence of God, consideration must be given to how moral values and good ethical practices might have evolved without being designed by a God.

---

[152] Since my initial draft of these notes, not putting the ball in straight is now accepted by the RFU. If you really cannot stop the cheating, redesign the game to allow it!

[153] It has also encouraged, even demanded, unethical behaviour from its followers in struggles for the supremacy of a particular religion.

[154] Paine, op cit.

I accept that the most significant cause of Man's physical evolution is the notion of the Selfish Gene, probably assisted by Genetic Drift and Recombination theory. I argued earlier that Man's own intentions had some effect too and will, I believe, become so increasingly. However, here I am looking well back in time and concerned with the major cause of the evolution of ethical practice. From many studies of living organisms, all have their main objective in life to reproduce their own offspring and, hence, continue their own gene pool, often even to the extent of killing off the offspring of other beings of the same species or, at least, fighting off rivals for sexual partners. There is no sense of ethical practice here. So why did the notion of ethics develop and are humans the only species to hold such values? It is convenient to discuss this question at three levels. First, if all organisms are in competition for survival, how is it that we see much collaboration around us? Second, how did fairness develop into a much the broader notion of social democracy? Third, how did feelings of compassion, which I argue below are separate from just fairness, develop?

The Development of Collaboration alongside Competition

I think it probable that, through evolution, certain species began collaborating within their own species and also, in some cases, with other species, as evidenced now by many instances in the animal world. Those that collaborated survived and multiplied through the advantages that they gained from that collaboration. Those that did not collaborate did not survive. Survival of the species is not the same as survival of the genes, but a being must survive into adulthood to provide progeny and, hence, is a prerequisite of maintaining the genes of those involved. Collaborative behaviour *within* some species is obvious. Collaboration in hunting ensured that food was obtained – evidence is widespread from lions and wolves hunting in packs to hunting amongst early humans who aimed to kill much larger animals than could be achieved by the single human individual. Once more, those that did not collaborate did not eat and did not survive. Collaboration can also be seen between different species. An obvious example is that of small fish helping to cleanse much larger ones.

Exactly the same logic can be applied to the growth of human communities with specialisation of roles within those communities. Also having a more developed brain capacity, Man was better able to perceive the advantages to be gained from collaboration. This does not mean that such collaboration, especially amongst humans, is easily given. Much will depend upon trust and that normally has to be built slowly. As Dawkins[155] says that if 'the shadow of the future' is long, better trust relationships are likely to develop.[156] Although he also says that this will be tempered by suspicion of betrayal. As the key to continued existence became agrarian practice, Man probably saw that it was beneficial to spend less energy on competitive conflict and more on forming well-organised communities. Man saw how to become productive employing specialisation (using what economists call the *Law of Comparative Advantage*) and, hence, generally more successful at reproducing their own kind. This was not the result of genetic codes, but of humans, *as organisms*, thinking out what they wanted.

Dawkins[157] pursues this a little deeper:

> Natural selection of selfish genes gave us (humans) big brains which were originally useful for survival in a purely utilitarian sense. Once those big brains, with their linguistic and other capacities, were in place, there is no contradiction at all in saying that they took off in wholly new 'emergent' directions, including directions opposed to the interests of selfish genes ... so we can sit down together and with language devise politics, ethics and values which are vigorously anti-Darwinian in their thrust.

Here, those that argue that Dawkins' Selfish Gene Theory suggests a picture of a red tooth and claw world that does not recognise human values that do exist in our world, have their answer from Dawkins himself! And yet, if *organisms* with larger brains started to modify a world of individualistic,

---

[155] R Dawkins, *Science in the Soul,* op cit, p 58.

[156] See also C Tomkins, Interdependencies, trust and information in relationships, alliances and networks, *Accounting, Organisations and Society,* Vol. 26, issue 2, 2001, pp 162–191.

[157] R Dawkins, *Science in the Soul,* op cit, pp 39–40. In the same book Dawkins provides a section entitled the Science of Values (pp 41–61) where he discusses this question at length.

ruthless competitive survival, I feel that, initially, they did that still in a very selfish way by collaborating to be successful in competition. That collaboration led to the growth of societies. This was, I believe, the beginning of the development of what we have come to consider ethical behaviour. While ethical behaviour is now seen in terms of an appropriate attitude towards other human beings (and animals), it probably developed in a selfish way through a realisation that well organised communities could not function without such collaboration.[158] To repeat, there is nothing in organisms doing this that is contrary to Darwinian or Neo-Darwinian Theory and, moreover, the whole process is rational.

From Fairness to Human Rights and Democracy

It is obvious that the benefits that society yields are not evenly spread. The fact that they are not evenly spread does not mean that they are necessarily unfairly spread. One may decide a fair distribution is not equal shares for all, but a system where benefits are allocated, say, in proportion to those contributing to their production. However, it is still obvious that very successful communities, in terms of power and influence, have existed where benefits were not spread fairly by any prescription. This has occurred wherever strong and powerful elites have dominated the rest the community to such an extent that its members could be forced to produce far more for the elites than for themselves. This is quite consistent with the argument above that collaboration evolved where beneficial. It is just that some part of the (selfish) community realised that, through its power, it could gain more

---

[158] Recall that Marx argued that it is not the consciousness of men that determines how they act, but the social context that determines their consciousness. This is consistent with ethical behaviour having evolved because it was necessary in the emerging social environment. There is much in this view, but given the discussion in the previous Section about the Extended Mind, I would prefer to say that action was the result of an interaction between consciousness and the environment. Marx did, of course, go on to considerably expand this view of historical materialism to predict that society as a whole was heading to communism. This extension has now largely been discredited and will be reviewed briefly in the section on political philosophy.

from the enforced collaboration of others. Nevertheless, if particular parts of society take significantly unfair shares of the benefits from the existence of that community, in time total collaboration will be difficult to maintain and the community will not work so well in providing benefits and even rebellion by the (selfish) unprivileged may occur. Hence, I am of the view that selfish motives played a part in the development of fairness and indeed democracy.[159]

The notion of fairness is of long standing. It is evident in Ancient Greek literature underpinning the writings of Plato and Aristotle on Justice. It probably goes back much further as even animals struggle to get their fair share of the kill.[160] It seems to be a feature of individual survival. It is interesting nevertheless to consider how the call for fairness emerged on a much larger scale and led to modern democratic processes. A brief reference back to some key events in earlier times in English history can illustrate this.[161]

After the successful Norman invasion of 1066, the Normans were quite fierce and demanding in their domination of the Anglo-Saxons. They formed an elite of barons around the king and did very little in terms of mixing with what the Normans saw as second-grade citizens. The general population of England was, hence, very dissatisfied with many serving a life near to slavery, but they could do little about it. Just over 100 years later, the king had become too autocratic, even for many of the barons, giving favours to French relatives and associates, rather than more widely distributing them amongst his barons. The result was that the barons rebelled and this led eventually to the *Magna Carta* in 1215. This did not spread benefits to the ordinary people, but did take steps to improve the position for the barons and free men, giving them, amongst other things, freedom from

---

[159] This part of Section 5 could equally have been included in the Section on political philosophy, but it seemed to arise from the basic need for fairness and so it was included here.

[160] At least younger ones do, often having to give way to parents as first sharers of the kill.

[161] I am not at all sure how this sort of development occurred in other countries, except, perhaps, France, with its revolution, and the USA with the War of Independence. Possibly Russia too, with its revolution, but the notion of fairness for all soon dissipated there.

illegal imprisonment and a limitation of feudal dues paid to the Crown.

Henry III then reissued the *Declaration* in 1216, removing the more radical parts and again in 1225 when he wanted more revenue in taxes. There was growing dissatisfaction this time in a wide section of the community, including many of low status, who were suffering from famine as well as their very limited freedom. This wider community was now prepared to request changes and act rebelliously if they were not granted. Led by Simon De Montfort, many barons, also still discontented, joined the cause, and the king was defeated at the *Battle of Lewes* in 1264. Subsequently, De Montfort, in effect, ran the country for a time. The king retained his title, but decisions now rested with the Council, headed by De Montfort, in consultation with Parliament. By the Second Parliament, each borough was invited to send two ordinary citizens to Parliament. The gains were short-lived because the king and royalists fought back and defeated and killed De Montfort in 1265. Nevertheless, De Montfort's short 'reign' is now seen, with the earlier Magna Carta, as the initial stage in the development of parliamentary democracy in England[162] and an early stage in the development of human rights which now have become a central part of modern ethics. In other words, while a powerful elite can force others into collaboration to further its own ends, in time the subjugated can themselves collaborate and take power to improve their own position.

Seven hundred years later,[163] a similar ethical stance has been taken by nations in formulating the human rights movement. The idea of human rights had evolved over centuries as the initial stages have just been described. By the mid-1900s, the idea of a much wider interpretation to human rights became firmly established after the Second World War when the UN, after recognising what took place in Nazi Germany,[164] issued a recommended

---

[162] The notions of freedom, protection of property rights, etc. are now fundamental to the English political system and even more explicitly to the USA Constitution.

[163] Of course, much was debated about human rights within this long period.

[164] Incidentally, Simon De Montfort cleared all Jews out of his earldom at Leicester and persecuted the Jews in London and elsewhere, confiscating their records for practising usury, then forbidden for Christians. He also cancelled debts due to Jews. So from a modern viewpoint, he could be seen as both a hero and evil.

practice to be applied for every individual, irrespective of creed, race, colour, geographical location, wealth or education.[165] Essentially this provided that all persons were born free and equal and should act in brotherhood, each had a right to life, liberty and security, each should not be subject to slavery, cruelty or torture and be considered innocent until proved guilty and not subject to arbitrary arrest and imprisonment.

Since then most countries have adopted their own treaties setting out their own stances on human rights. There is much that could be discussed on this topic and various philosophers have debated different aspects of human rights, but the key point to be addressed here is: Why did the notion of human rights develop? At first sight, such behaviour in search of fairness seems a long way from being driven by competitiveness. The De Montfort illustration makes clear, however, that the initial impetus came about through collaboration to compete for the welfare of a wider section of society. A large number of people identified with a group (peasants and middle rank subjects) who saw themselves as different from the ruling class. They exercised competitive power to ensure a fairer distribution of resources. In a sense they acted selfishly, but not unreasonably, in order to secure fairness. Perhaps then, possible elites also saw the benefit of social cohesion to avoid the costs of disruption or even revolution. This might have entailed the recognition that one would not be allowed into life's competition unless one was also prepared to accept responsibilities to ensure others could join in. But it is clear that a firm sense of fairness has entered the public psyche. Fairness and ethical standards have evolved, without any help from God, through a tortuous path from originally competitive motives. There was no need for an ethical spark of fellow feeling to be implanted in humans by some God-like intelligent source, although fairness is now an almost innate part of human consciousness.

Moreover, the struggle for fairness still continues. While good human rights practice is now accepted by most countries (but not all), there are still major issues where large sections of society feel they have a separate identity and are not treated fairly. An obvious example is the feeling among

---

[165] *Universal Declaration of Human Rights*, United Nations General Assembly, 1948. The description above is very truncated. The Declaration includes 30 Articles of rights.

ethnic minorities that they are disadvantaged and, indeed, treated badly by authorities such as the police and other parts of the law and order process. This has not developed into outright revolution as used by the peasants in the examples above. Nevertheless, from time to time sizeable demonstrations occur – usually sparked off by some particularly visible instance of injustice which emphasises differences in identities.[166] This is, perhaps, the most striking illustration of potential conflicts over fairness between major identities within society, but there are others if less potentially explosive. For example, there seems to be a sense of difference in identity between the North of England and the South, leading to the recent Governmental promise to level up wealth and opportunity for advancement between these regions. Many, especially the younger generation, have demonstrated across the world for action on climate change. To some extent, the younger members of society see themselves as a separate identity simply because they will be around longer and see what they feel will be terrible consequences for them if climate change is not pursued. It is clear, therefore, that a search for fairness stretches from the individual up to large groups within society which feel they have a separable and disadvantaged identity. More recently this has come to be called Identity Politics which will be reviewed later in this text.

For the moment it has just been established, at least to my own satisfaction, that ethical values could well have developed within a world driven *fundamentally* by competition and rational steps taken by Man, with his increased brain power, to modify that with collaboration and social systems of fairness. Initially, Man cooperated and formed improved organisation of their society, mainly against natural elements and other species, in order better to survive. Then elite groups within Man took unfair shares and were gradually deprived of them by those less well-off combining to exercise power and create a more equitable distribution of resources. Much of this collaboration is derived from a selfish motive and the need to compete, but that does not mean that such action always unreasonable. This competition may be against the elements (extreme weather events, plagues and diseases),

---

[166] The death of George Floyd at the hands of the police in the USA is an obvious recent example, but earlier examples have occurred in the UK, USA and elsewhere.

competition between nations, political philosophies, businesses, group or individuals. The level of cooperation and coordination needed obviously depends on the identities and type of threat involved. Collaboration can enhance competitive ability where appropriately applied. Moreover, one can expect to see collaboration and fairness being observed within groups in allocating resources gained from competition. Fairness and collaboration is multilayered in line with the level of society with which one is concerned.

It is also clear though, despite the movement of human rights and efforts taken to deal with major issues like the rights of black people, climate change or regional differences, some sections and members of society will still be disadvantaged, perhaps due to sickness, poverty or other experiences. Then those not disadvantaged may well feel a sense of duty or moral obligation to help the less fortunate. Moreover, as discussed in the earlier section on consciousness, most humans do experience physical emotion when perceiving those in great distress and some degree of (higher) satisfaction if they do something about it – not in a self-congratulatory sense, but rather with a sense of duty or, perhaps more often, with pity. In times of real and extensive hardship, one comes across many examples of people helping out others and sharing what limited food or other resources they have. The widespread practice of contributing to charities is an offshoot of such feelings and thinking. This may have resulted from a long run conditioning on the needs for fairness in a smooth functioning society, but there seems to be more to it than this.

The Source of Compassion

It is clear that instances occur where people are prepared to take quite extreme steps to perform what is seen as duty and even severe personal sacrifice, when they do not appear to have a direct benefit for those individuals themselves.[167] A prime example is the often widespread public personal sacrifice taken

---

[167] This is not confined exclusively to humans. A recent TV programme showed how monkeys organised themselves to distract a leopard which had cornered another monkey. The other monkeys put themselves at considerable risk, but did enable the monkey that had been trapped to escape.

in times of severe threat such as war or a pandemic of disease.[168] Also, at such times too, people seem to be much more willing to express feeling and regard for their fellow men and even help them without any obvious benefit in return. How can such actions be related to the previous argument that collaborative practice is derived from the need to be competitive and fairness from selfish principles? It could be argued that, where the threat is very severe, people realise that, if there is not widespread collaborative resistance to it, all will suffer badly. In contrast, if resistance is pursued, not so many will suffer and one has to take one's chance that it is not oneself. In that case the basic motivation is still the need to compete with the threat, but those wishing to see off the threat must play a probabilistic game with regard to their own personal safety.

But that still does not explain the urge for more fellow-feeling at such times when there seems to be a deep desire by many to help and share resources with those less fortunate. It may be due to the feeling 'there, but for the grace of God, go I'. In which case there is a strong ring of fairness about it. However, that is still not an adequate explanation.

To address this further, it is necessary to note that there is quite a difference between being fair and having compassion and these two concepts have probably evolved quite separately. Both fairness and compassion require empathy – the ability to see the other person's position. However, the concept of general fairness seems to have been derived from both the capacity of collaborative groups of citizens to hold powerful elites to account. Compassion suggests something more.

To be compassionate, one obviously needs empathy, but having empathy does not mean that one has compassion. One also needs to have a desire to do something about the position of those less fortunate, often at a cost to oneself. Moreover, as already mentioned, being compassionate involves

---

[168] At the time of writing just after the anniversary of VE Day, we have been reminded of the extensive sacrifice made by many during the Second World War and we are also in the midst of the 'lockdown' required to constrain the Covid-19 virus pandemic where, not only have people had to make sacrifices in terms of freedom of movement, but also many hospital and care home staff have had to risk contamination to serve those in need – often, initially, without appropriate protection equipment for themselves.

personal emotion. Indeed neurologists have discovered parts of the brain more involved in compassionate behaviour. A research report[169] in 2006 concluded that altruism was not a superior moral facility that suppresses selfish urges, but is a fundamental characteristic hard-wired into the brain and can be quite pleasurable. If this is so, it suggests that the compassion had a rather different cause than fairness which, I have suggested, came about through *rational* action to organise a more fair society. This is not meant to imply that compassionate behaviour is not influenced by direct experience of hardship or witnessing it. No doubt our personal attitudes towards compassion are being refined all the time by experience. There does, nevertheless, seem to be a case for arguing that the possession of a basic capacity for compassion is hard-wired into the brain.

If compassion is innate in the human brain, what caused it to evolve? This seems to be a very important matter to address when considering debates about the role of competition, collaboration and compassion in society. Certainly, if compassion is hard-wired into the brain, it must have happened a very long time ago, early in Man's evolution, and long before the societal struggles for power that led to widespread adoption of fairness with modern-type customs, laws and rules.

Supporting this thesis, there is also recent evidence that the Neanderthals practised compassion to help the injured and sick with no apparent self-interest involved.[170] If that was so, the hard-wiring must have occurred long before that. Spikins[171] provides a number of specific examples of discoveries that show strong evidence of compassion amongst Neanderthals and early humans.

One possible explanation goes back to notions of consciousness and, in particular, of identity. As the first small collaborations of our ancestors occurred to assist in the survival process, it is possible that members formed

---

[169] Human fronto-mesolimbic networks guide decisions about charitable donation, *Proceedings of the National Academy of Sciences*, USA, October, 2006. See also comments in the earlier section of this pamphlet on the brain where it was stated that separate areas of the brain dealing with rational argument and emotional responses have been identified.

[170] P Spikins, A Needham, L Tilley, G Hitchens, Calculated or caring? Neanderthal health care in social context, *World Archaeology*, 2018.

[171] P Spikins, *How compassion made us human*, Pen and Sword Books, 2015, pp 67–75.

a clear identity of their incorporation into a specific group or family. Such groups may have developed a somewhat stronger sense of togetherness, than the collaboration, at that time, needed simply to hunt or have better organised society. Group practices beyond just hunting must have occurred such that individuals identified with the group and its interests and this included taking care of those less able to do so for themselves. This may have been because it was recognised that those disabled, if cared for, could still contribute something like care of the young or home maintenance and even hunting again if they recovered. Or it might have been because the older disabled had played a part in bringing up the current active group members and close bonds had developed between them. Whatever the reason, it probably occurred in some mammals (e.g. primates) somewhat before the emergence of humans, or even Neanderthals.

Obviously, I have no proof that this is the explanation for compassionate behaviour, but it makes sense in at least two ways. First, a person's compassion seems to diminish the further the distance from those suffering. The further the suffering from the observer, one may still be aware that it occurs, but cannot see what it is like. This lessens the emotional response. This suggests that the basic emotion of compassion is naturally localised to the 'close family' or local group. The advent of charitable advertising on TV and indeed the more widespread reporting of news from across the world, has partially changed this and so the scope for compassion reaches further afield. Second, it does appear that compassionate and charitable events occur continually which cannot be easily associated with furthering selfish competition (even in groups) or establishing a more ordered society.

An alternative or additional explanation may be that empathy which enables compassion was hard-wired into the brain even earlier before thinking organisms learned to live in larger groups. Even association with one other needed for sexual and other life activities needs empathy with the significant other[172] for agreement to these activities. This may have led to thinking organisms becoming conscious of any pain, discomfort or unhappiness in the significant other when it had experienced or imagined something similar

---

[172] Who may, of course, been temporary.

itself. This may have led to compassion for the other party, perhaps through concern to maintain the relationship or just general sympathy.

The explanation of how compassion evolved will probably never be clear. One can agree with Dawkins (see above) that once we had brains we could use them for all sorts of life choices other than mere selfish behaviour, but that alone does not explain why compassion was probably hard-wired into those brains so early in the evolution process – probably far earlier than the development of language or choices made regarding aesthetics or social organisation or, indeed what one might call a higher level of ethics introduced to maintain fairness and constrain excessive forms of competition. Moreover, nothing written in this part of the text undermines Darwinism, for as well as introducing the notion of natural selection, Darwin addressed the subject of altruism. Spikins[173] states that Darwin, himself, thought that human altruism was explicable by evolutionary processes and even inevitable once any animal reached a certain threshold of empathy. The more subtle question is when and how during the process of evolution, progressed by natural selection, did different types of current human values other than just competitiveness develop. I obviously have no ready answers and can only suggest some ideas related to this puzzle, but in doing so I think it clearly confirms for me that we should not criticise Darwinism and Neo-Darwinism as indicating the world progresses *only* according to ruthless competition.

The Problem of Conflicting Moralities and Brief Historical Review

Turning now to consider the context of ethical decision-making in more detail, complexities arise where there are competing moralities where a simple reference to being fair cannot resolve the issue. An oft quoted case is where a person out walking along the coast with a young son or daughter sees that someone in rough water is in danger of drowning. Which is the greater obligation? To attempt to save the person drowning and risk one's

---

[173] P Spikins, *How compassion made us human*, op cit, p 173.

own life, or stay with the offspring recognising the position one would put them in if one did drown oneself. Moreover, the issues do not just arise at an individual level. At corporate level there is the ethical drug issue. To what extent should company experimentation be permitted on animals and humans to develop new medicines. Furthermore, at a Governmental macro-level, should one promote recovery from recession by increasing expenditure through substantially increased borrowing thereby throwing an increased obligation to meet the debt on future generations? Of course, the resolution of this issue is not straightforward – much depends upon what the money is spent, whether it will enable future generations to be better off and how that is evaluated compared to current hardship. A very important variation on this theme is the current (April, 2020) dispute about whether it is better to employ tight social distancing and business closure rules aimed to reduce deaths and illness from the coronavirus disease or to relax or even abandon them in order avoid the scale of a subsequent recession which itself would entail increased poverty, illness and deaths, particularly from other diseases like cancer, heart attacks or diabetes. Resolving such an issue is not straightforward, especially given the uncertain knowledge associated with either option. Clearly governments worldwide are seeking a 'fair' balance, but it is a significant moral dilemma with a variety of views on what is appropriate and, hence, leads to political debate.

There is also the totally different issue of whether it is ethical to tell 'white lies' on the basis that more harm will result from the truth being told than not.

There are many ethical puzzles that one can construct for which there is no absolutely correct answer and which can only be resolved by human judgement. In fact, the key ethical issue in such cases is really making sure that all the consequences of the alternate actions are properly considered and communicated by those with responsibility for taking the decision and, in addition, ensuring that the decision-maker has a well-developed sense of ethical behaviour, fairness and justice.

One should also remember that views on ethical behaviour can vary over time as well as over different current contexts. For example, to the Ancient Greeks, ethics had a different emphasis than modern moral philosophy.

Aristotle[174] emphasised the difference between a life that is praised and a life that is prized. For Aristotle, moral behaviour was certainly to be praised. Indeed it was expected that someone well brought up would act morally as part of his nature without needing to give it much thought. Even so, someone who follows a *eudaimon* life is to be congratulated. It seems, however, that Aristotle's *Eudaimon* is a complex concept. It incorporates moral behaviour but, in addition, includes all elements required to live a good and flourishing life.[175] He said that involves wealth, good looks, being well-born, honour and achievement and he says that one cannot be *eudaimon* if one is ugly, lowborn solitary or childless.[176] These factors are, however, really those associated with an ability to spend a life, first, in rational contemplation and, second, in political life involving public office. These are the crucial features of *eudaimonia*. Then, strictly, the degree of *eudaimonia* achieved by anyone cannot be completely assessed until a person's life is at an end.

Moving on to medieval society, moral philosophy was discussed extensively by Augustine, Abelard, Aquinas, etc. who considered much more than being fair. They discuss concepts of lying, murder, sex and whether it is immoral to intend to undertake an undesirable act as distinct from actually doing it. They all, however, bring a different emphasis and relate these notions to God and eventual happiness in heaven. Much of our current views on morality can be traced back to these religious origins.

Ethics then took a different direction in the 16th and 17th centuries. As discussed in Kenny,[177] Luther and Calvin emphasised the depravity of human nature and that happiness can lie *only* through faith in God and not in human systems of ethics. In contrast, Casuitry, whereby moral principles were applied to specific situations, addressed issues like usury and the treatment of slaves in the newly discovered America. The Jesuits countered

---

[174] J Urmson, *Aristotle's Ethics*, Blackwell, 1988.

[175] Urmson, op cit, says many scholars view *eudaimonia* as personal happiness, but he thinks this is too simple an interpretation of what Aristotle meant.

[176] See Urmson, op cit.

[177] A Kenny, *The Rise of Modern Philosophy*, Oxford University Press, 2006.

Reformation ideas and made themselves particular authorities on Casuistry issues and leading confessors to hear and form opinions on situational sins. The Jesuits were later opposed by Pascal who thought equivocation around the truth, probabilism (finding someone, anyone, in authority to validate an action) and explaining action by way of a praiseworthy intent rather than the true intent, were despicable Jesuit practices. Later Hume argued that justice was based on the need for society to function (much as I discussed above in seeking the source of moral values) and Kant stressed that the core of morality was the performance of duty – Aristotle's *eudaimon* virtues of fortune, courage, intelligence, Kant said, could all be used to bad ends. This was followed by Hegel who tried to synthesise the opposing views of Aristotle and Kant and also laid emphasis on the way moral behaviour depended on the societal context.

The 19th and 20th centuries saw the development of utilitarianism (actions should be taken to provide the greatest happiness for the greatest number) through Bentham and Mill, although there was a difference in emphasis between the two. Some critics saw this as too strict in specifying that morality could only be evaluated by reference to a notion of the total universal happiness which was impossible to evaluate, while others saw it as too lax as its refusal to have absolute prohibitions suggesting a flexibility of choice with no clear standards of behaviour. Schopenhauer and Kierkegaard from their respective atheistic and religious standpoints both call for the subjugation of the self and pessimism of human ability to pursue a highly moral life. Nietzsche, in very marked contrast, shows some sympathy with Aristotle's concept of a worthy Man, but goes far beyond him. Nietzsche advocates the development of a flourishing Superman who is the ultimate that Man can achieve through the power of exercising his will. For Nietzsche there was no room for Christian-like support for the weak or failures. The Superman is one who is strong with a will to exercise power and promote the elevation of the species to the most able level. Conventionally listed virtues do not assist in Nietzsche's version of the good life. Moreover, Nietzsche states that this end will not be achieved by biological or social evolution without Man's own will for it to happen.

Taking a quite different line, Hare separated the notion of ethics from morals. To Hare, ethics related to prescriptive and universal statements of what one ought to do, whereas moral judgements relate to specific actions and contexts. Anscombe subsequently pointed out that statements of universal 'oughts', based on the notion of duty and moral right and wrong, were all based on Hebrew-Christian philosophy and so had no logical underpinning if one no longer held a belief in the Hebrew-Christian God. It would be better, she argued, to focus on justice in specific contexts and return to an approach based on eudaimonia whereby morality was based on human well-being with no need for a lawgiver such as God. Rawls, in the USA, rejected utilitarianism as a means of preventing injustices and, like Anscombe, advocated a focus on the development of a system of justice based on fairness.

What is the point of this highly truncated listing of past philosophical references? Well, I first set out above what I believe to be the everyday layman's way of intuitively thinking about ethics in terms of fairness and also fellow feeling. By listing some key developments in ethical thought through history one can see contrasts in views, but also dominant themes which still pose questions for today. What part should religion or notions of universality play in current moral philosophy? Kant would also distinguish between his emphasis on duty and the Aristotle/Nietzsche axis of *eudaimon* Man and Superman, although, where Aristotle calls for those able to pursue a public office, I think he is not so far from Kant. There is the contrast also between absolutism and relativism – are there universal moral laws which should always be upheld or can the appropriate moral action only be judged by reference to context, whether historical, societal, economic or wartime? Is it better to eschew all virtues based on religion or even the notion of a universal will of Nature and try to develop a humanitarian system of justice and fairness? There are several conclusions that I would like to draw and also suggest how society might structure its approach to ethical issues.

First, as will be clear from my section on God and Religion, I reject God as a fundamental justification for human moral behaviour. Moreover, one cannot, if one does not believe in God as portrayed by at least the main Western religions, use the largely medieval philosophical literature as the unquestioned basis for 21st century moral behaviour. I feel, nevertheless, that many conventional virtues like fairness and concern for the less fortunate as espoused by religion, *are* appropriate indicators for behaviour in current times because they arose in recognition of the need for them with the evolution of well-organised societies necessary for the continuation of the species and gene pool. Religions and religious leaders, despite their claims, were not the originators and justifiers of these ideas, but took on the obvious needs that were developing anyway and used them to try to organise societies for the better while, perhaps, ensuring that they themselves did the organising. The *Ten Commandments* did not, in my view, come from God, but from Man's perception of what society needed to function. God was brought into it to provide authority and as a threat to make Man comply. But, it does not really matter how moral values developed. If society needs them in order to function, the important point is that they are observed whoever claims the credit – whether religions or not. A revamped 'Religion', without the ritualistic reference to a human-like God, has an important part to play in our society.

Next, what relevance does the *eudaimon*/duty debate have now? It is clear that it is in the interests of society that most men and women try to achieve their potential. This includes the creation of wealth and standing in society. The more wealth that is created, the more is available for all if properly distributed. At the same time, the achievement of standing in society will reflect the contribution that one has made to it. This may be through public service or through many other occupations. The key point seems to be that this wealth and public standing should be strived for through personal effort but *must not be achieved unfairly*. It should be a moral requirement that there is 'a level playing field for all'! This is not to undermine the need for competition for wealth or public office. Competition should ensure that the best emerge, but the competition must be fair. I cannot see why the notion of *eudaimon*, updated to reject its assessment by level of birth, cannot be consistently applied with a concern for one's fellow men and women and the aim to do one's duty by them.[178]

---

[178] This would obviously reject Nietzsche's Superman with no real concern for his fellow man.

Next, consider the question of absolutes versus consequentialism. It also seems clear to me that whatever the act, even if it involves killing, theft or other very serious offences, one cannot say *absolutely* that there will *never* be a context where such an act is not appropriate for a moral person. However, some acts, like murder, are so extreme that it is *most unlikely* that such action will ever be justified.[179] It will enable society to function smoothly if, as a pragmatic device, that society ordains that it is absolutely forbidden to undertake such acts. Hence, society will always want to be informed and be committed to examining the case and considering punishment where such an act arises. In modern Western society it will always be possible to appeal and state one's case why any penalty for such a breach is not justified, but it should be seen as very much the exception rather than a widespread practice. Hence, state laws are formed relating to crimes and other forms of organisation may well adopt similar absolute rules and rule breaching consequences. Other than in these extreme cases, however defined, moral behaviour will have to be assessed consequentially as much of modern philosophy seems to advocate.

More modern philosophical thought seems to be that one should seek justice rather than attempt the definition of specific acts as morally desirable or undesirable. This is a natural outgrowth from considering the context and consequences of actions and should be the preferred approach to dealing with philosophical conundrums. Fairness to all those involved should become the key criterion for making judgements and not some impractical notion of the aggregate goodness. But this also begs some questions. Is fairness any more measurable than aggregate happiness? One has to determine whose position needs to be judged and by what criteria. The notion of identity is crucial to determining this. Unfairness is a difference in benefits derived or costs incurred by different groups or identities. To resolve such issues one needs to understand what the competing identities are and what they are seeking. Then, with even more difficulty, how the competing needs and consequences have to be balanced between the parties involved. However,

---

[179] Even then some would argue that State sponsored murder to protect the realm or acts of war are justified.

without first getting a very clear recognition of the competing identities and their goals, resolution is likely to be difficult.

There can be also be different perspectives on what is fair and, it is clear, that large variations have occurred over time. The appropriate and acceptable treatment of women, ethnic groups, homosexuals, old people, prisoners, animals, animal hunting, abortion, euthanasia and so on is quite different now from earlier times, at least in some contexts. Similarly, different parties to a dispute (e.g. divorce proceedings) can have markedly different views as to what is fair and just. Consequently, one needs rules to use, not in specifying moral behaviour per se, but in attempting to establish justice. As indicated earlier, this will surely involve an open consideration of all aspects of any moral dispute with the help of established experts in overseeing such judgements. There is the whole panoply of legal practice which tries to achieve this, but, even where it is deemed unnecessary to go to the courts for a judgement, there are established ways of conducting formal and fair evaluations as discussed by people such as ER House or E Guba and Y Lincoln.[180]

Even if one has established and reliable evaluation procedures, there is still a problem. A great many human actions involve moral issues. One could not possibly address every one with a formal evaluation, in the same way as one could not take every issue to court. So, many moral issues have to be taken at the level of individual conscientiousness, possibly aided by views of friends and colleagues when necessary. If one wishes, therefore, to minimise unethical behaviour, it will be necessary to instil a sense of moral responsibility into all of us humans. It becomes important to develop a moral conscience through education and upbringing[181] with, perhaps, an associated disapproval by one's fellow men where moral breaches occur. Even then, such instruction cannot be left to the consideration of a series of specific case studies, though they may be part of the instruction and used

---

[180] See for examples amongst many, ER House, *Evaluating with Validity*, Sage Publications, 1980 or E Guba and Y Lincoln, *Effective Evaluation*, Jossey-Bass, 1981.

[181] It could be argued that it is obvious that a well-functioning society needs certain ethical standards and that every effort should be made to apply these, irrespective of how they came to exist or might change in future.

as examples. As a matter of pragmatics, one will need to specify *categories* of behaviour that are desirable and undesirable, even if one recognises that one can never specify absolutely how one should behave in any situation. Such categories might include avoidance of cheating and how that is defined, care for one's fellow men and women, especially those less fortunate than oneself, attitude towards race, age discrimination, avoidance of lying, playing one's part in social gatherings, paying one's share of taxes, animal hunting only for food or protection of property etc. In fact, consideration of these issues has led right back to the beginning of this section where it was suggested what ethical behaviour now means to most people.

An Ethical Structure in Society

The above arguments also suggest that there is the need for a societal and educational *hierarchical structure* which encourages widespread moral behaviour.[182] First, there are matters which require an absolute specification by the State that no breaches of certain rules will be tolerated, next there will be issues which do not require legal sanctions, but which require formal evaluation of justice and penalties, then lower down the structure, issues should be decided by individuals based on education and current opinion about specified categories of behaviour. At the lowest level in this hierarchy there will be some highly specific situations which cannot be classified into the accepted desirable types of behaviour and which must be determined by each individual on the basis of more general features in his or her upbringing. For practical reasons, the moral society must depend on a mixture of absolute rules, proper judgements and individual responsibility. There is, perhaps unfortunately, no universal Bentham-like measure of welfare that can serve as the basis for such assessments, although the notion of maximum benefit for all does have value in reminding us that all in society have a right for their position to be properly reviewed and considered.

There is a final caveat to be presented. All of this argument was based

---

[182] I now take this to include both fairness and compassion. Entities of all sizes from governments down to individuals can act with compassion.

on the need for a well-functioning and civil society which itself was needed for the evolution of Man as a species. One must recognise, however, that there will always be a tension between acting morally, however defined, and individual or group interest. The way society evolves taking into account these pressures has nothing to do with genetic variation working in tandem with natural selection, but is the product of many human brains giving thought to the problem. Although there could be a sense in which it is natural selection in that Man may adopt such procedures that, with experiment, seem to work best. Also specifying what moral behaviour is does not answer the problem for the individual of how much of it to apply. It is one thing to say one must do one's civil duty (however that is defined), but how much time should one spend doing that compared to making one's own living? How far should one go in attempting oneself to correct inappropriate behaviour observed elsewhere? That can only be decided by the individual's thinking subject to societal pressure of thinking by others.

In addition, one should be aware of how values change over time and also beware the *complete* specification of morality by a political or religious elite or even the State. There will always be the need, in Socratic fashion, to remain sceptical in the sense of being prepared to re-examine the current system of moral guidance and whether that fits with the current context. Without this, emerging elites may use their own specification of the moral system to dominate and serve their own interests which can lead to a society that functions less efficiently for the majority. There will always be elites. Indeed they are needed to provide leadership and organise action, but they must be always open to question.

In ending this Section, two other observations are offered. First, in order to ensure widespread ethical practice and a well-functioning society, there is an obvious need for a hierarchical structure including Government instructions, treaties, the legal system and mandatory rules, evaluation systems and education to promote individual responsibility. This reflects the varying needs for collaboration across different interest levels. In other words, there seems to be the need for a combination of moral prescription by a lawgiver, though not now in the form of God, and the need for individual responsibility to build a worthwhile life (eudaimonia). Even then the lawgiver approach will only operate effectively if widely reviewed and accepted by most members of society. Such a system is well established, but is always in need of review and, where necessary, modification.

Second, from early days all major religions, Western and Oriental, recognised that their adherents should where appropriate be fair and compassionate.[183] In fact, this seems to have become the main message of the main religions. This is welcome, but their justification for existence by reference to God was like their explanation of the real physical world being the creation of The Almighty. With what we know now, there is good reason to argue that, as with the universe, it is unlikely that fairness and compassion resulted from divine influence.

It does need to be emphasised, however, that religions have played a valuable and central role in getting society to its current state. Most religions have had their blemishes throughout history, caused mostly by extreme zealots or powerful men using religion as an excuse for aggression. Religions have, however, provided a continuing basis for how one should live and participate in society. For many, however, at least in the West, religion seems to be at risk of losing its position of influence. It could regain this, first, by leaving aside the justification for its own existence based on an unknowable and higher authority.[184] Religion can still give guidance on behaviour to its congregation and continue valuable teaching on care for others, fairness, kindness and need for forgiveness. It could do this more effectively by adopting an improved social role indicating *specifically* where there is *greatest* need for fairness and compassion for the disadvantaged. After all, pleas for help and charity are in competition for resources with both other charities and wider demands for financial support. Also, it does not need a concept of God or reference to the Bible to justify this. As a more developed conscience of the nation, this extended role might include acquiring a

---

[183] The exception, perhaps, was the more robust approach to the less fortunate exhibited in Ancient Greece and Rome.

[184] It might be argued that if no recognition is made of God, there would be nothing that could be called religion. But, if my suggestion is what religion evolves to, why not keep the name and build upon the existing religious institutions?

better understanding of rigorous evaluation approaches in examining calls for compassion and charity. Religious institutions do not necessarily have to conduct the evaluations, but they would need to understand how they should be made and raise debate to ensure that such evaluations are made. In addition, it would be necessary to examine claims for charity from both a statistical and a qualitative perspective – first, to assess how widespread the problem is and, second, to provide a better understanding of the nature of each type of suffering, its degree of severity and its implications. Religious authorities should not be expected to make definite decisions (they probably would not be allowed to do so), but they might act independently to ensure decision-makers are *fully* aware of the impact of those hardships on all concerned and the costs of rectifying them. It is doubtful whether many religious clerics (vicars, bishops, etc. and their Moslem and Jewish counterparts) would currently be very willing or competent to do this. However, a religious authority could establish something like a 'fairness and compassionate needs research unit' with selected staff or clerics trained in such skills. These units could report to religious leaders to make their pronouncements more precise and considered. Religion could then really become an independent conscience for mankind and an unbiased movement for the greater good, which is, I think, what it always wanted to be.[185]

Empathy

In rounding off this Section, it seems important to address briefly the concept of empathy and to distinguish it from ethical behaviour. Empathy is basically collecting information about what others think and feel. Of course, as pointed out earlier with references to Nagel's bats and Searle's

---

[185] The Christian Church has, of course, other key roles. It uses its ritual and ceremony to celebrate national joy (e.g. after winning wars or when there are royal weddings, etc.) It provides a venue for wedding and funerals. There is no reason for this to change. And, if some want to relate these events to worship of God, that is their choice. Whatever I think, there is little harm in it and to some it may give comfort. But I do think that the church could provide a key role in a more organised and pragmatic way of identifying where compassion is most needed.

robotic computer, one can never have a total grasp of what it is like to be another being or be absolutely sure of what they feel or are thinking. Nevertheless, it is quite clear that one can often gain quite deep insight into what it must be like to be the other person (but not the bat or computer!). If we do not, it is difficult to see how social interaction could take place. It is also difficult to see how ethical behaviour can exist if there is not empathy, but ethical behaviour is not the same as empathy. Having discovered what the other person feels one may decide to ignore it. Ethics concerns acting to address the issues of fairness and compassion. One may act ethically without immediate empathy where it has become established custom to act in a particular way, through religion or otherwise, or as ordered by law, but there must originally have been a sense of empathy by someone for that custom or law to have been established. If religious representatives undertake more developed roles as mentioned above they will be providing an improved basis of empathy to enable better ethical judgements to be made.

6.

Aesthetics and Recreation

Despite the heading, aesthetics and recreation are clearly not the same thing, but are both treated in this Section because they may have similar implications for governing organisations as dealt with later. Also both seem to have resulted, as suggested earlier in this text, when Man found that he did not have to spend all of his waking hours seeking food or competing to survive. He needed to find something to occupy his mind. One is reminded of Dawkins, once again, when he said that brains developed for the purpose of surviving could be used for other purposes. He even says that there is nothing inherently implausible in inheriting genes for particular aesthetic values.[186] He also reminds us that adoption of different values can be built in by breeding. Cave art may, of course, have had a purpose beyond decoration and been much more closely linked to survival. Spikins[187] says that now Palaeolithic art is explained more as a means of information gathering and communicating knowledge about hunting practices. One can imagine a cave dweller standing in front of a cave wall, like a schoolteacher with a pointer, indicating to youngsters where to attack a wild bison to minimise the chance of injury. Nevertheless, aesthetics relating to art as a form of beauty and satisfaction almost certainly developed from cave wall painting and music, perhaps, from some early form of singing or instrumentation that was undertaken to give warnings of danger or safety. It is not difficult to see how such matters were essential to survival then, but they were also activities to employ the brain using capabilities such as sight, hearing and physical dexterity which had already evolved to aid survival. In contrast, a more general recreation like sport may well have developed from games used to practice skills needed to catch prey or fight rival tribes which did aid evolution and survival. Another leisure activity like reading for pleasure was

---

[186] R Dawkins, *Science in the Soul*, op cit, p 54.

[187] P Spikins, op cit, p 34.

an offshoot of developments in spoken and then written language which had also developed as an aid to coordination of activity.

Aesthetics

The Cambridge English Dictionary defines aesthetics as the formal study of the principles of art and beauty. Aesthetics means beauty and good taste in fine art.

I have always liked looking at art in the form of paintings and pictures and engaged in oil painting myself in a very amateurish way. I stress that I am not an expert of fine art, but I know what sort of art I like. Is that, however, being aesthetic? I think not, aestheticism must relate to more than just liking. I turn, once again, to Kenny[188] to give me a basis for thinking about this topic.

Kenny summarises a number of views in aesthetics from the initial coining of the phrase by Baumgarten in the mid 18th century. To Baumgarten the purpose of art was to provide something beautiful defined as an ordered relationship between parts of a whole. The purpose of that beauty was to give pleasure and arouse desire. Soon after, Burke and then Kant introduced the notion of 'taste' and that the idea that disinterest in the usefulness or value of art was fundamental in the assessment of that art as aesthetically attractive. They agreed that beauty in art has itself no purpose, the production of beauty *is* the purpose of art. Others question this as described below.

Prior to the Romantic Poets, around the outset of the 19th century, attention had focused on the reaction to art by its consumers. The Romantic Poets, especially Coleridge, stressed that the creativity lay with the producer of the art and it was the emotion generated in that person that really counted. The artist attempted to transmit the emotion he/she felt to give pleasure to the art consumer.

Schopenhauer supported the notion that desire must be absent from works considered to be aesthetic. He also thought art should be beautiful, but saw it as having several levels with the lower bound being something

---

[188] Kenny, Volume 4, op cit, chapter 10.

charming and the upper bound being something sublime. Something of average beauty we can contemplate without any major surge of emotion, but something is sublime if initially it creates a strong emotion within us and, in reaction, we have to struggle to reach a state of calm contemplation. He gives examples of pictures of a storm at sea or raging waterfalls.

Nietzsche viewed art as detached from actual use in a different sense. He viewed the purpose of art as an escape from the tyranny of life. Whereas, Tolstoy thought that art could only be good if it portrayed a moral purpose and that moral emotion was shared between the artist and the consumer. According to Kenny, this view was largely abandoned in the last century when the beauty of art was deemed to be its own purpose (Croce) irrespective of any moral intent. Collingwood then emphasised that beauty was not mere amusement. Nor could just a crafted object with a clear practical purpose be considered aesthetic. If art has an objective, it is in articulating the preconscious emotion of the artist before and during the creation of the work and revealing it in a way that can be shared with others. Wittgenstein, however, rejected art as a communication by the artist. He reminded us that we can never know exactly what emotion the artist experienced in creating the work. We may think we know what the artist meant and felt, but we will never be able to experience feeling at the time of creation. Later philosophers then emphasised the independence of the work of art from the author. For the consumer of art, art is what it is and what he or she makes of it.

Collingwood stated aestheticism seems to be more than mild entertainment or amusement. It is something more than charming and near to the upper reaches of Schopenhauer's range of beauty. It has also to be something more than a fleeting sensation. An image of beauty must be something that reinforces one's view of it as delightful as one repeatedly contemplates it. An object or action providing contemplative delight is therefore a thing of beauty. On the whole this contemplation does need to be separate from the thought of any immediate satisfaction of personal desire, although, after much contemplation, a person might desire to possess the item in question subject to practical considerations. The beauty must lead to the desire, if at all, not the other way around. It is perceived first by our eyes and then internalised through our senses and brain.

So with contemplative delight in mind, what art forms are available via which senses? There are several, but the obvious first is painting and associated forms of pictorial art. Wittgenstein was clearly correct in specifying that the viewer can never really know the emotion felt by the artist. One might get closer to it, I suppose, if the artist were present and explained in detail how the work was developed and completed, but this is rarely possible and more often than not the artist is already dead and experienced a different age and environment. So what makes a painting aesthetically beautiful? It must, at the very least, be the interaction of composition and colour to give a delightful visual expression. The perception of the harmony between these attributes will vary from person to person, but there is probably a sense of harmony (or discord) in any painting that resonates with many people even though it may be difficult to put into words. Such a general reaction may have something to do with an inherent notion of a natural order of things possessed by human beings even though this is a vague expression. Moreover, this should not be taken to mean that an art object is only aesthetic if it simulates nature.

While harmony of form and colour are important, that is not all there is to art. Often the artist includes symbols giving clues as to what he wants the viewer to think about. These symbols may even be meant as puzzles for the viewer. Consider *The Ambassadors* painted by Holbein. One might agree that there is a certain beauty in the form, detail and colour in the two figures in the painting and so, on the definition above, the painting would be considered aesthetic. Does this apply, however, to painting of the many artefacts, including the skull which can only clearly be seen from the side and above? Any sense of harmony there is rather loose and not particularly delightful in a visual sense.

Moreover, all painting does not attempt to portray natural physical beauty and much of it is meant to disturb the senses. One only has to look at the range of different painting styles to see that different artists have been trying to communicate different things and not necessarily present works of beauty at all.[189] This suggests that art is more than just perceived beauty.

---

[189] Traditionally, art mostly portrayed people and scenes in its natural observable form

The artist still gains personal satisfaction and pleasure from the process of creating art, but the viewer has to understand the artist's motive. Aesthetics in art, therefore, involves both the artist's stimulation derived from the creation process and also the art critic's judgement on the extent to which the purpose of the painting was met. Moreover, in addition to different styles, there is a range of painting techniques.[190] The critic can try to evaluate how well those techniques have been applied, whether in terms of use of colour, brush strokes, free expression, etc. It seems, therefore, that aesthetics is not just about beauty (though much of it is and, many, including myself, place a greater store on what I think are beautiful paintings than much modern work). It is also about the appreciation of fine art in terms of its construction and purpose.

So far this discussion of aesthetics has focused on painting. Indeed aesthetics is usually defined as such. We do talk, however, of beautiful music and physical movement. So should we not widen our definition and incorporate into our understanding of aesthetics the ways in which *all* of our senses may register something delightful. Extending this line of logic; art, ballet, poetry, rhetoric, theatre, novels, music (in various forms), architecture, movement as in dance or even gymnastics, mathematics and possibly some aspects of sport could all be considered aesthetic because they create a feeling of delight by means of one sense or another. The reader may be surprised that gymnastics, mathematics and some aspects of sport have been included, but some types of gymnastics require great care to perform movement gracefully and elegantly, mathematics may produce an elegant proof, and there may be long and flowing movement in some sports which are a delight to see. Does elegance equate to aesthetics? This

---

(excluding early art portraying God and angels). But the last two or three centuries have seen a spawning of different styles with different purposes. There is now Modernism, Impressionism, Abstract art, Expressionism, Cubism (now a subset of Abstract art, but it preceded work of artists like Picasso), Surrealism. Such styles are meant to make the viewer ask questions about form. In the case of surrealism, it is meant to shock. *The Scream* is a good example. Few would claim it is beautiful, but it was meant to shock not be pleasant to look at.

[190] Oil, watercolour, pastel, acrylic, matte, spray, graffiti.

seems to be a matter of definition and trying to capture in words what intensity of emotional response justifies calling something aesthetic. In my view, following the recognition that the essential attribute of aesthetics is giving the producer and the viewer emotional delight, the definition should encompass a wide variety of phenomena. What is core to the concept is whether a person experiences a feeling[191] of delight in producing the product or taking part in the activity and, also, if the consumer, after careful contemplation, also experiences delight irrespective of through which sense or combination of senses, that experience was derived. The sense could be eyesight, hearing, touch, taste (in the sense of taste of food) or the brain.[192]

The inclusion of taste may also be controversial. The words 'good taste' are often used in respect of aesthetics, but can one say that a dish of food is aesthetically attractive because of its delightful taste? And can a dish which is visually attractive[193] be considered aesthetic even if mediocre in taste? One can argue this two ways. First, one can agree with Collingwood and say that a crafted object is designed for a purpose and so is not aesthetic just because it is well made.[194] Cooking would fall into this category and so could not be considered aesthetic. On the other hand, if the taste gives real, and quite possibly, unexpected delight how different is that from hearing several chords of delightful music? Perhaps the word 'aesthetic' should only be applied where the emotional delight is intense, but that still does not solve the problem because taste can be very intense and, furthermore, how does one evaluate intensity of feeling – especially comparatively across different senses?

---

[191] Penrose, *Shadows of the Mind*, op cit, says that the essence of aesthetics is human feeling and that cannot be replicated by a computable machine trying to model consciousness.

[192] Care is required not to be absolute in advocating 'delight' as a criterion. Delight might be taken by some in causing pain to others, winning a commercial battle or even gaining revenge for a previous defeat by an old rival in a sporting event. A line must be drawn somewhere, such satisfactions obviously cannot be viewed as aesthetic.

[193] The Japanese, in particular, place great store on the art of creating an attractive appearance for food put before one on the plate and this practice is spreading in the West and so perhaps one can.

[194] Such an argument would seem to apply to architecture as well.

One obvious problem with such a wide definition is that it entirely ignores the degree of education or experience possessed by the consumer of art or other activity. The phrase 'connoisseur of fine art' is in fairly common use. This implies that the consumer has undertaken time and exercised effort to study the type of material for which he/she is known as a connoisseur. This raises the question of whether experts can provide an objective, or at least a broad consensus, on what being aesthetic is. Can there be some absolute standard? I think not, for all the reasons specified above. I do not believe that one can measure the feeling of delight felt by one individual in a way which can be quantitatively compared to that of another. A connoisseur may need a much higher standard of composition to delight him/her than someone with no real knowledge of the subject matter. The more one understands about the art/work in question, the more scope there may be for deriving joy from it. Agreeing with Hume[195]; all expertise in assessing the form and beauty of objects are not equal. He said that expert connoisseurs show better delicacy of taste, wide experience and practice in evaluation which most of us do not possess. We can learn from experts and, thereby, enhance our experience in the same way as one learns higher skills and knowledge from a good teacher.

Similarly, recent philosophy has apparently tended to leave the artist aside to focus on the work itself as having aestheticism if it creates an emotional response from the consumer. It is obvious, nevertheless, from the many who get involved in creative artistic activities on the production side that they do get much emotional delight from being the artists. Moreover, attempting to create art can itself be a form of education which leads to better appreciation of the art of others. Those who have participated in learning music and performed in operatic productions, even if only local, will have a better sense of the delight to be obtained from different operas than others. From my very minor dabbling with oil painting, I now look in a different way and much more closely at old masters and get more satisfaction from them.

Clearly different people will have different views on what they think of as aesthetic and I find it difficult to accept that their exact feelings can

---

[195] D Hume, 'On the standard of taste', *Selected Essays*, Oxford University Press, 1985.

be compared in any precise quantitative manner, but general orders of magnitude might be determined by evaluation approaches mentioned earlier when discussing whether one can assess what it is like to be another person and empathy. Also my conclusion is that one should not define aesthetics too narrowly. There is no harm in labelling a branch of philosophy as aesthetics and taking it to mean simply all those human objects and processes that give delight to contemplative people in creating or appreciating a range of art forms.

Recreation

Like aesthetics, recreation[196] is not immediately related now to survival or bodily needs. Only a relatively small percentage of the population earn their living from aesthetics or recreation. I have much sympathy with Nietzsche when he said art was a release from tyranny of life. This suggests it enables the person involved as producer or consumer in art to escape from the daily turmoil of life in something pleasurable, even if only temporarily. But so do many other forms of amusement and entertainment. This chimes again with comments earlier that discussed how humans developed the need for higher satisfactions when they no longer had to spend all their time just managing to survive. Like the heart, the brain cannot switch off or we are dead. So it employs itself on what is pleasing to it. Many may employ this time on matters which may be considered aesthetic, but probably many more will spend time on other activities which Collingwood would term 'mild entertainment or amusement'. This might include playing sport, reading, exercising, tending the garden, watching films or TV, meeting friends, eating out or, indeed, anything which does not involve what can be called one's main occupation or career. These activities are no less important than aesthetic activities. They are a requisite for a healthy human existence. Even connoisseurs in fine art will need to spend some time on such activities. Such activities are required to maintain physical and mental health. At some time most of us experience stress and anxiety over our

---

[196] As distinct from exercise.

work or other matters, or even just overwork. The ability to cope with such pressures will vary from person to person, but most will need, from time to time, to be able to 'switch off' and relax. We can then return to our prime tasks, recharged and ready to face what they offer. The brain cannot 'switch off', but its focus of attention can be diverted through the operation of its own Mind. If those organising parts of our society promote or allow space for aesthetic activities, they should also recognise the need for some leisure time. Some people are in such dire straits that they are struggling the whole time just to survive. This is, perhaps, less common than was the case in earlier centuries, at least in the UK and other developed countries. Current welfare systems do, indirectly, enable some such persons to have some leisure time. An advanced and stable society does need to bear in mind the need of its citizens for some recreation. Yet, care must be taken not to make too clear cut a division between work and pleasure. Many find considerable pleasure in our work and find that we do not need as much 'pleasure time' as others. This will depend on the nature of work at which one is employed and each person's disposition and opportunities.

Aesthetic delight is not the same as the more general phenomenon of pleasure. There is, however, no neat boundary between what is aesthetic and what is just pleasurable, apart from the intensity of feeling. Aesthetics concerns the more refined end of a continuum of activities that involve giving human beings pleasure and entertainment.

I have suggested that aesthetics and indeed other forms of recreation arose partly from the need for survival, but also out of Man having surplus time from that necessary to survive and needing to occupy his Mind. This is not, however, an explanation of why we see the mixture of 'non-vital activity' that we do in society. Why do some prefer to spend their time painting while others play sport or watch television? How do they choose a balance between these 'other activities'? There is an obvious choice that can be made. The choice made will depend in part on genetic make-up, part on personal background, part on persuasion of others, part on opportunity and so on. Within limits imposed by such factors, each individual presumably spends time on what he or she finds most satisfying. To understand aesthetics and recreation choices fully, it is necessary to study the biological determinants of the thrust of joy or excitement at seeing a painting that one likes and, say, scoring a goal at soccer. Surges of such enthusiasm must come for the brain, but how is it driven? Also, what enables the brain to choose between low satisfaction activities (that one generally likes) and those with high satisfaction (that one is excited about)? This takes us right back to a consideration of the Mind. There is room for more philosophising on this subject.

7.

A Worthwhile Existence Revisited

When I began thinking about writing this text, my aim was, using Kenny's books, to outline the main areas of philosophy and then explore what I thought of for each area. This was in line with my assertion that anyone, however well or undereducated, would have a view on each area even if those views were not outwardly expressed. Of course, I recognised that the very act of thinking and writing down my views might change those previously held tacitly and to a limited extent they have. I was drawn into further enquiries in some areas, especially on some interfaces between science and aspects of philosophy. The few changes in my views will, however, be left for the Conclusions at the end of this text. Having reached the end of Section 6, I realised that the areas of philosophy and science already reviewed, *taken in combination*, can be used to explain what a worthwhile life is and also explain human behaviour when taking major decisions – ones which are strategic to existence. In addition, the factors involved in this decision-making are equally applicable at the level of the individual, the organisation (charities, businesses, etc.) or Government and State level. Hence, it is also relevant for holding public bodies and Government to account.

I am aware that the notion of a worthwhile life has a very long historical heritage, dating back to Plato, Aristotle and even beyond. Furthermore, it underlies much of subsequent philosophical thinking and became very explicit in the writing by Nietzsche in his different perception of what a worthwhile life was in his discussion of Man as Superman. The notions of a worthwhile life proposed by Aristotle and Nietzsche seemed, although quite different from each other, to advocate a universal standard for worthwhile behaviour to which everyone should aspire. They did recognise that different individuals will have different degrees of success in achieving those standards, but they argued that everyone should strive for the same things.[197]

I suggest that this universality is not borne out by human behaviour. What is considered to be a worthwhile life will vary from individual to individual and from organisation to organisation. Individuals have quite different lives all of which could be considered worthwhile. So, if there are many variants of a worthwhile existence, how should they be identified? Surely the perception of a worthwhile life lies within the individual person or organisation. Of course, others may see the worthiness achieved by any individual or organisation as rather different from that entity's own perception. The important question is how does the individual person evaluate how to run a worthwhile life and evaluate success in doing that? In some respects there will be a very wide agreement on factors that must be present in a worthwhile life. These will concern compliance with well-established laws and social conventions. However, there will also be a huge amount of variation in what individuals think of as a worthwhile life stemming from their own understanding of who they are (identity), what values they hold and what possibilities they perceive. They will be influenced by other's view on them in the way an individual's Mind is influenced by outside sources, but, at root, they will have their own perceptions of worthwhileness which will guide their behaviour. It follows that each individual will be striving for different things. They will all be striving for survival, but what a satisfactory survival means will vary from person (or entity) to person (or entity).

There may be difficulty with the application of this approach where the individual is very severely handicapped. Also doctors have medical ethics to try to help them and parents make horrendous decisions regarding significantly premature births or patients with other extremely severe

---

[197] I am very aware of my layman status in making the following argument. There may have been much in philosophical literature, or even in the other writing of Aristotle and Nietzsche themselves, of which I have no knowledge and which discusses variants of definition of a worthwhile life. Yet I feel that my brief review of different areas of science and philosophy leads to the interpretation of a worthwhile existence that I now propose. If it is 'old hat', so be it.

disabilities.[198] Doctors can hardly know what such babies would consider to be a worthwhile life and, I presume, have to rely upon some more universal guidelines to make such decisions over life and death. However, what I am proposing is not the use of universal indicators, but the use of a few guidelines to specify what *each individual thinks of as a worthwhile existence for himself or herself*, given bodily traits with which they have been endowed or can develop. Thus a handicapped person may seek a very worthwhile life in, say, music.[199] Of course, many disabilities are much more severe than his, but most disabled people would, I believe have some idea of what would be better for them. It is only where their thinking capacity is severely limited, that the idea of them thinking through what was a worthwhile existence for themselves is unreachable.

So we may take it that most individuals do have a sense of what survival means for themselves and here survival can be interpreted as achieving a particular style of life. This includes a choice of wealth or, following Aristotle, public service but also personal and family relationships and their intensity, career, fame, ethical outlook, degree of ambition, and willingness to exert effort compared to enjoying recreation.[200] Each individual will be striving for a mix of these achievements and it is success in this combination of factors that will produce satisfaction or not about achieving a worthwhile life.[201] Following this line of argument it is possible to set out quite a simple description of how we all behave when making key decisions aimed at giving us a worthwhile life. This description does not offer precise measurement or what is a right and wrong decision. It will simply offer a set of headings which have, so far, been discussed separately in this text. This list is relevant both in aiding decision-making and in offering accountability for decisions

---

[198] This was pointed out to me by Dr Diana Green who kindly read an earlier draft of this text.

[199] Andrea Bocelli is a superb example. Part of the world was closed off to him, but, my goodness, he has made a very worthwhile existence of that open to him.

[200] Although different recreations will have differing degrees of effort associated with them.

[201] Of course, some of these goals may be tacitly held based on a ready acceptance of aspects of our identity such as physical attributes, birthright, social standing, or limited knowledge of what we could achieve.

made. This list applies equally to individuals, organisations or governments in considering strategic matters.

First, stemming from our basic physical nature (as emphasised by the Selfish Gene Theory and the way our cells must compete to survive) _Competition_ is vital for human progress. This applies throughout the whole structure of life: at cellular, individual, national and global levels.[202] My meaning of competition here is inclusive of all forms of competition needed to survive whether against states of nature or human rivals. We have to compete against the forces of nature to protect ourselves from viruses (very evident with coronavirus recently), earthquakes, floods, global warming and much else besides, some of which to occur in the future may be quite unknown. We as individuals also need to compete against each other to a varying extent to gain and maintain employment, nourishment, security, finding a mate, protection of our family and other needs we may have. Organisations, such as charities[203] and businesses have to compete to advance their cause. Governments and politicians running them must be aware of competition from war, trade or other means which threaten the livelihood of their citizens. Success in competition is an important item in my list of requirements for a worthwhile existence. Without it, other desirable attributes have no foundation. Ability to compete must, therefore, be part of achieving a worthwhile life.

The call for competition to survive begs the question of 'As what?' When considering surviving at a fundamental level, it is a truism to say that this means staying alive, but when considering the need for competition in human activity at individual, organisation or State level, this does not make sense unless the decision-maker states what goal s are being sought. To be clear on these matters, it is necessary to have a clear concept of _Identity_. One major consequence of consciousness is our view of self-identity. Clearly,

---

[202] It also seems to be inherent in our DNA – witness the widespread involvement in sports. It is also interesting that some sportsmen and women seem to favour single competition while some favour team games requiring much collaboration.

[203] Even claims for compassion by charities compete with each other as well as non-charitable activities for the limited resources available.

what we think we are and what values we have, influences our decision-making and behaviour. So underlying much of human behaviour and the way humans compete is the notion of Identity.[204]

It will also be valuable if the identities of our rivals are understood.[205] This is not just who or what they are in a general sense, but what are they seeking and what can they do to cause us difficulty. This calls for considerable _Empathy_ – trying to put oneself in the other's position. Empathy must be a key item on the list. As I am including natural disasters as a form of Competition, it follows that I must use a very broad interpretation of empathy which includes understanding thoroughly the nature of crises due to states of nature as well as what exactly human rivals are seeking and how they might go about achieving it.

The latter has long been recognised in business literature on corporate strategy where companies are advised to consider both their own and rivals' strengths and weaknesses and threats and opportunities. This general level of advice was also extended in considerable detail, some time ago, in books such as those by Porter.[206] Identity is, therefore, another factor explaining behaviour as it is only after clarifying identity, ours and that of others, that it is possible to understand what degree and type of competition is needed. It also suggests, again following Aristotle, an emphasis on using careful reasoning to guide our lives and even a Socratic stress on the need to question existing practices is vital in achieving a worthwhile existence. This is relevant at both individual and organisational level.

---

[204] There seems to be some growing criticism about the development of Identity Politics, especially where identity groups are infiltrated or even taken over by elements aiming for radical disruption of society. My suggestion here is, however, that all decisions are taken with an underlying sense of identity and so a consciousness of what identities are affected by a decision is important. I do not approve of a manipulative adoption of Identity. Claimed political Identities should be examined for homogeneity amongst its apparent members and have their interests discussed fairly. This is another topic to be discussed later.

[205] In the case of a Government this will include other countries or bodies posing a competitive threat but also rival political parties wishing to gain power.

[206] M Porter, _Competitive Strategy: techniques for analyzing industries and competitors_, The Free Press, 1980 and M Porter, _Competitive Advantage; creating and sustaining superior performance_, The Free Press, 1983.

While one may succeed in competition for some time using one's existing strengths and power to restrict others from gaining them, in the longer run, one will not succeed without _Innovation_. In Wagner's view, Innovation is a central feature of *all* evolution. In his interpretation, it existed in the form of new chemical reactions which took place before life began, but it certainly occurred with the development of evolution by means of genetic change which enabled improved competition for life. Those with the best improved genes survived. It is also clear that to remain competitive any person or organisation must be prepared to be innovative if they are not to fall behind in the social competition to survive, earn a living, be successful at business, outcompete other nations, etc. The need for innovation may be in response to a crisis caused by natural disaster or others adopting new practices or inventions. Most individuals and organisations experience a crisis of some type during their existence which requires a modification of their activity. The current coronavirus pandemic is an obvious example, but there are many other possible crises such as an individual having a serious illness in the family or being made redundant, a company losing a key market or a country losing a war. Alternatively, a person or organisation, with no current crisis, may attempt continually to innovate just to stay ahead of the competition or forestall the effect of a possible future crisis. There is no doubt, however, that innovation is required for continued survival. Innovation is, therefore, another critical item for the list.

So, to achieve a worthwhile life, we decide what our identity is, look at the competition that threatens it and what innovation is needed to maintain it. However, this is not necessarily a lone activity. As discussed in addressing the topic of ethics, _Collaboration_ is often needed to be successful in many forms of competition. It is absolutely vital when society faces major threats like wars, pandemics, etc., but the degree and type of collaboration and assistance needed clearly depends on context and the nature of competition required. This applies at international, national, business, group or individual level. Countries form alliances and trading deals with other countries, governments need the cooperation of its citizens to achieve many of its goals, companies develop associations with other companies in the form of supply chains or distribution networks, individuals seek collaboration through trade unions, clubs and other forms of association. Collaboration is another item for the list.

As suggested in the Section 5 on Ethics, the widespread acceptance of observing fairness in human life resulted mainly from a rational process to ensure social cohesion and has led to a general vehicle by which to assess many aspects of ethics, especially including human rights issues, although many ethical issues may never be resolved beyond question and new issues will always be arising. All individuals and organisations are faced with ethical issues which influence how we behave. It may be thought, at first, that fairness is not very relevant in business decision-making and that success in competition overrides all, but that would be wrong. The law tries to ensure that there is fair trading (e.g. by setting trading standards) and also provides a legal framework to provide justice without which companies would not have the same business environment. It is in business interests to maintain this. Employers also need to observe fairness in dealing with employees and customers and suppliers. Otherwise they may not obtain any cooperation needed. The majority of society therefore seems to accept that fairness is, therefore, to be considered in decision-making.

Ethical behaviour moves beyond just fairness where compassion is needed. There seems to be, as argued earlier, a deep internal and human physical reason for compassionate practice which is different from the rational competitive approach which led to fairness. Being competitive does not, however, need to contradict being compassionate. They are two separate human attributes that have evolved alongside each other. Also, those most successful in competition may accumulate the resources to be best able to act where compassion is needed. Compassion should be considered in decision-making where proposed actions affect others who may be less fortunate. *Ethical Behaviour* needs to be added to the list, incorporating needs for both fairness and compassion. Also religious beliefs clearly affect the behaviour of many people and so these must be included in ethical influences. In order to act ethically, fairly and, where appropriate, with compassion, it is important, once more to have considerable empathy with those affected by any decision one will make. We all exhibit empathy in its literal sense of collecting knowledge about others. We use this knowledge to gain an appreciation both how to compete or interact with them taking into account their ethical predispositions, on such things as fairness, compassion and religious beliefs.

Finally, the last item on the checklist is _Recreation_ where this term is taken, rather broadly, to include any desire for aesthetic satisfaction or other leisure pursuits. As argued in the previous Section, a key concern of individuals is for some form of diversion or recreation. As such, the need for this pursuit must be recognised as a driver of behaviour and recognised in decision-making.

So, to summarise, individuals all have a sense of identity and what goals they want to achieve in the competitive environment which they inhabit. For most individuals the goal will include bringing up a family, achieving financial stability, success to some degree in a career, acting ethically, deciding what type and degree of recreation they need taking into account uncertainties associated with all these matters. These are all matters comprising their identity. Where competitive pressures threaten that identity, individuals also need empathy to understand the identities of the threats, both from natural events and human rivals. Armed with such information, individuals will be in a position to decide what innovation and/or collaboration is needed to compete successfully. The action decided upon will always be subject to some form of ethical constraint, which may stem from a deep sympathy with certain others or simply compliance with laws and generally observed practices for ethical standards. A similar sequence of steps in decision-making can be observed in individuals or organisations of all types.

It could be said that all this is obvious. After all, it is what individuals and organisations do already to achieve what they see as worthwhile existences. I merely offer the following list to indicate factors to review when making key decisions and assessing accountability. The strength of this list is that all items on it are directly linked to different areas of philosophy. So, to achieve what we think of as a worthwhile life for _ourselves_, we need be conscious of:

IDENTITY (to include our ethical disposition regarding fairness, compassion, religious beliefs and desire for a certain standard of existence and recreation)

COMPETITIVE ENVIRONMENT

EMPATHY (with those with whom we compete)

INNOVATION

COLLABORATION

Achieving a worthwhile existence means, surely, attaining the goals helping to form one's identity or, if necessary, achieving goals modified to cope with a changing competitive environment. Empathy, Innovation and Collaboration are tools by which this may be achieved. It is suggested that for both individuals and organisations one can use this checklist of five factors to:

(1) ensure decision-making is thoroughly conducted and

(2) evaluate whether a worthwhile existence has been achieved

(3) judge where decision-makers are to be held to account.

Careful consideration of these five concepts can take one a long way when trying to explain and evaluate individual and organisational performance, but precise measurement is certainly not suggested for any of them. Also, this is hardly a new approach to making key decisions. It is really just showing how existing decision-making reflects different key areas of philosophy. As stated, people and organisations must already make decisions involving these factors in their struggle for survival and a better existence. However, that does not mean that decision-making by any individual or organisation cannot be improved.[207]

---

[207] It is interesting to note that at the time of writing this there has been much criticism of the Government's handling of the Covid-19 crisis. I have no wish to comment upon the merit of those decisions which were and still are being made where there is considerable uncertainty as to outcomes to be derived from different action. Calls for more hard evidence before making decisions have been numerous when there is little hard evidence to be had. However, as argued by Sumption (*The Telegraph*, 3 October 2020), the decision process has not been as open as many people would like. If ministers had been required to explain what information they had and on what basis every key decision was made, with wider feedback before action was taken, better decisions might have been made together with wider agreement and collaboration reached on what needed to be done. As Sumption pointed out, part of the problem may also be that The House of Commons cannot set its own

There is one very important caveat that should be made. In the literature on corporate strategy very detailed analysis, for example like that suggested by Porter (as mentioned above), is sometimes questioned as risking inaction through overanalysis. Brunsson[208] argues that, where there is considerable uncertainty, extensive analysis will only emphasise that much uncertainty exists and reduce commitment to action. He therefore suggests that businessmen take decisions based on 'action-rationality' (i.e. on an impressionistic basis combined with analysis of just a few options) provided the decisions are generally consistent with the business's overall ideology. I suggest that this applies to individuals as well. In terms of terminology used in this text, ideology can be taken to be reflected in identity. Certainly, the point needs to be made that, if a person or organisation has a strong sense of identity, a lot of the thinking and/or prior experience would usually have led to that identity.[209] Then appropriate decision-making on empathy, innovation and collaboration is more obvious and taken more quickly. Hence, it may well be that key or strategic decisions do not need to be made very often. However, from time to time crises will occur that call for significant innovation and even a change in defining one's own identity. Then more analysis will, in most cases, be required.[210] The reader may recall the similarity of this argument with that in the section on Biology where it was acknowledged that life was not *continually* about competition if not needed, even though, at root, competition was needed to survive.

---

agenda which is set by the Leader of the House, and the Speaker. Others have little influence and so this limits accountability. Sumption, though, clearly does not support the view that a 'strongman' is needed to ensure necessary action is not impeded by endless debate and negotiation over who benefits or loses most.

[208] N. Brunsson, in *The Irrational Organisation*, John Wiley, New York, 1985.

[209] I repeat, much of identity may be inherited or adopted in line within one's social context without much thought, but a reasoned examination of who one is, one's beliefs and goals is more likely to lead to actions to satisfy them.

[210] For business settings this is discussed in C. Tomkins, *Corporate Resource Allocation*, Basil Blackwell, Oxford, 1991. The same form of logic applies to individuals and other forms of organisation like Governments.

8.

Political Philosophy

Political philosophy is concerned with the purpose of Government and its relationship to its people. It is concerned with how Government is organised and how it should use its power to protect the rights of its citizens. It has not been so concerned with the mechanics of Government, such as voting systems or with what specific Government policies should be, but with arguments for what ought to be the driving forces for defining Government's role and how it should go about developing its policies. Answers to these questions need to draw upon earlier comments on the need for competition, the need for collaboration, ethics, the need for coordinated action and social cohesion and compassion, and human pleasure where appropriate. This section shows how the main driving forces for establishing the Government's approach to its role have been largely established by past philosophical debates (at least for Western democracies) and that will be illustrated first. That will be followed by a consideration about how specific policies should be developed in our modern environment drawing upon the discussion in Section 7.

A Brief Historical Review of Political Philosophy

According to Kenny,[211] the heyday of political philosophy was from Machiavelli in the 1500s through to Hegel in the early 1800s. It was during that period that attention focused on 'the abiding core of pure political philosophy', whereas, afterwards, more modern political philosophers related their ideas to the emerging disciplines of economics and sociology. I shall, therefore, start simply by listing the views of political philosophers as explained in Kenny's Volumes 3 and 4.

At the time of Machiavelli concern in political philosophy was

---

[211] A Kenny, op cit, Volume 3, *The Rise of Modern Philosophy*, 2006. This review depends very heavily upon Kenny's texts.

predominantly for the role of the State as it existed in Italy at that time. Machiavelli makes clear that the prince should be an aristocratic ruler with main concern for the existence and welfare of the State. The prince must appear to be virtuous in order to retain control, but he should, above all, be feared and be as manipulative as necessary to achieve his ends. Machiavelli argues that a prince may want to have a reputation for compassion rather than cruelty, but he must take care not to make a bad use of compassion:

> a prince must not worry if he incurs reproach for his cruelty so long as he keeps his subjects united and loyal ... it is far better to be feared than loved if you cannot be both.[212]

He continues, however, that his behaviour must be tempered by humanity and prudence and that he must not seize the property of his subjects and their women and he should strive for high esteem. By doing so, he can avoid hatred and subversion by his subjects. There are two main things with which a prince must be concerned: internal insurrection by his subjects and aggression by foreign powers. So one does see, in what Machiavelli lists as the first main concern, some limited recognition of subjects' needs and fairness as earlier reflected in Magna Carta and The Peasants' Revolt in England, even if these ideas are not progressed far. This is often left aside in stressing his advocacy of manipulative rule.

In contrast, Thomas More, writing at about the same time, imagined a world where the family was the main unit of society. Property would be held in common with everyone, having a designated craft, having to work and maintain themselves based on simple needs – only scholars, priests and elected magistrates being exempt from manual work. This certainly recognises the need for community welfare, but it seems to advocate fixed class roles. Moreover, despite their obvious differences in approach, both Machiavelli and More argue for a totalitarian version of Government social control.

Around the beginning of the 17th century, Suárez, using ideas derived from Aquinas, focused on the second of Machiavelli's main princely concerns, being prepared for war. Suárez asked: when is war just? He

---

[212] N Machiavelli, *The Prince, section XVII*, Penguin Classics, 1961.

stated that war was just where (1) it was declared by a lawful authority (i.e. a sovereign state), (2) there must be a just cause[213] and (3) the proper means of conducting the war is available and the action was proportionate to the need. Hobbes, writing soon after, did not see war as an occasional requirement as Suárez had done, but as a basic condition of human nature. Recognising the centrality of competition as a feature of survival, he said that men will always be in competition with each other and there will be a perpetual war of man against man unless an overarching power is created to regulate their affairs. Man has to give up some of his individual freedom and to allow others this same freedom in order to avoid ongoing confrontation.

The only way to do that, Hobbes thinks, is for Man to cede control over key matters to a single man or body of men whose rule must be absolute and unquestioned. Such a system, however, would not be totalitarian because the system would exist for the benefit of the State's citizens and men would have freedom over matters where that the authority did not restrict that freedom by a law.

Spinoza, writing at the end of the 17th century, agrees with much of what Hobbes says, but he thought that man might well cede power to a higher authority in order to create a better context for life, rather than just to avoid warfare. He supported democracy, rather than other forms of authority and did not support the doctrine of the divine right of kings. He felt that absolute and unquestioned power should never be given. Also the authority should be held to account to ensure it acted in citizen's interests.

One is reminded of Paine,[214] writing over 100 years later, where he savagely criticises the English Monarchy about the time England lost America:

> In England a king hath little more to do than to make war and give away places … a pretty business indeed for a man to be allowed £800,000 a year for and worshipped into the bargain.

---

[213] This seems to be a mere truism if one is trying to justify when a war is just! However, he continued that war was justified if one's State was attacked or it was the only way to correct a serious injustice. Even then it would be just only if there was a high probability of victory, otherwise the exercise would be pointless.

[214] T Paine, *Common Sense*, 1776. This pamphlet supports the American revolution against the then English king.

Paine certainly did not feel that there was a divine right to be king. One wonders whether he would hold such extreme views about the constitutional monarchy now, although it is a fair bet that he would still advocate republicanism.

Locke, in contrast, focused more on the need of a superior authority to help preserve property rights. The Earth was not in the common ownership of all mankind, but allocated to individuals according to the labour that they had applied to the land. Locke advocated a group of trustees to act for the community with this group removable from power if they failed in that trust. Rousseau, also taking a more positive view of human nature, stated that a central controlling body was required to monitor property rights as society developed from a primitive state, but he emphasised that it was not easy to specify how the general will or requirement should be identified. He said it could be obtained by plebiscite if every voter was fully informed and that voters were kept apart so that no subgroups formed to influence the outcome. Unfortunately, neither of these conditions could be completely applied in practice.

Coming later, Hegel maintained that it is only through the competitive self-interests of individuals that 'the ideal destiny of the world' can be achieved. The State must therefore be formed to facilitate this and it is not just for keeping the peace or protecting property rights. War for him had a positive value insofar as it led to questions about that status quo and the search for better arrangements. He advocated constitutional monarchies at the head of nation states.

Moving on to the philosophers mentioned in Kenny's Volume 4, he says, pure political philosophy became fused with economics and sociology. In the late 18th century Bentham offered his greatest aggregate happiness principle as a guide to Government policy making as outlined earlier in a previous section this text. As argued there, this principle is quite impractical essentially because it offers no solution for weighting competing interests in the distribution and aggregate measurement of happiness. As Kenny points out, however, Bentham made significant contributions in other areas. Kenny gives Bentham's views on State punishment as an example. Bentham rejects using punishment as a payment of penance for the wrong committed. Punishment is only justified if it acts as a deterrent for either the wrongdoer or other potential wrongdoers, but while this is the main purpose of punishment it will, Bentham admits, sometimes be necessary to remove the wrongdoer from society by imprisonment or even capital punishment.

Coming after Bentham, Mill was very concerned that no Government or even public opinion oppressed the individual if that individual's actions did not affect others. He particularly supported free speech and writing provided that did not incite harm to others. He was also an early champion of women's rights insofar as they should not be legally subordinated to husbands.[215]

Probably the person having the most impact upon political philosophy in the 19th century was Karl Marx. His 'historical materialism' presented the view that the prime determinants of human behaviour were the factors of production (materials, labour, technology, etc.) available at any phase of human history and the relationships between economic agents employed in each phase. The latter was not open to human choice, but a function of how the factors of production were channelled into use. The phases of social evolution suggested by Marx were, first, primitive communist tribes acting as collectives who individually owned no land or property, this was followed by, second, slavery and then, third, feudalism which were appropriate means of organising such production that occurred in those phases. Eventually this was followed by capitalism which would inevitably collapse giving way to socialism and then mature communism. Capitalism would collapse because the capitalist bourgeoisie would only pay their workers (the proletariat) sufficient for their subsistence needs and not the value created by their labour, while keeping the remaining gains from production for themselves. This would lead to revolution by the proletariat with all property being taken over by the State. Eventually the need for a State itself would fade as the general consensus for a widespread communism with a coalescing of

---

[215] Kenny also describes Schopenhauer's opposition to women's rights about this time. Schopenhauer argued that women did not have men's reasoning powers and should not, therefore, be given equal rights. Indeed, he was in favour of polygamy. This view is now seen to be so outrageous that it will be considered no further in these notes. As Kenny says, we may be grateful that Mill's views and not Schopenhauer's are now generally adopted.

common and individual interests became established.

While of considerable influence leading to major upheaval, especially in eastern European states and Russia and China, Marx's predictions have not been accurate. First, in those countries advocating Marxian procedures, such 'communists', while removing most property to State ownership, have not managed to create an identity between all individual and common interests. Perhaps this was always likely to fail given human nature. Moreover, it is clear that these 'communist' countries have seen fit to maintain their own political elites, sometimes taking most extreme steps to ensure they survive. Capitalists too have acted in ways that make any move to complete socialism or communism less important for most of the population. Capitalist employees have been rewarded at above subsistence levels and institutions and asset holding arrangements have developed to the benefit of those employees (e.g. stock market investment, pension schemes.) Furthermore, the production gains available to all society has increased more under capitalism by enabling and encouraging entrepreneurship and creativity through competition in contrast to that achieved in centrally controlled communist bureaucracies. The pie may not have been shared out as fairly as some might like in a perfect socialist/communist state, but the pie was somewhat bigger and labour has benefitted as well as the providers of capital.

Following the Second World War and in reaction to the acts of totalitarian States of Germany, Italy and Russia, Popper was prominent in arguing that all State institutions should be capable of reviewing their operation and strive for continual improvement. It takes more than Government election by a majority to achieve this. Elections have to take place within an open society with free informed discussion and criticism of existing and proposed Government policies and the possibility of changing the Government and those policies without violence if necessary. Popper recognised, however, the need for Government compassionate intervention to help those less fortunate.

Finally, Kenny points out Rawls' attempt to set out a systematic theoretical structure for a liberal democracy. Emphasising that the welfare of society could not be allowed to override principles of justice, Rawls stated that everyone should be allowed extensive liberty and that there should be equal opportunity for all in competition for the higher positions in society, subject to an undertaking to take care of the most in need. He recognised clearly that one could never get a complete consensus on all issues, but, like Popper, he feels that the best arrangement will be for societies to encourage reflection and discuss differences in the correct frame of mind to achieve general agreement on what is acceptable given the competing interests.

A Brief Reflection on the History of Political Philosophy

Clearly the description of political philosophy above is highly truncated and itself reflects my very limited exposure to the many authors who have written about this topic over the last 400 or 500 years. Nevertheless, I hope that I have identified enough to be able to offer a reasonable summary of the general trend in this literature over time and a view on where political philosophy had reached by the mid-20th century.

It is clear that, at quite an early stage in development of Western countries, there was recognition that the king should not have absolute power over what he did. Kings and queens eventually accepted that they were not in position by divine right. Since the 18th century, the British monarchy has been transformed. It no longer holds the reins of power over State policy and acts in a largely ceremonial role. At most, it is a safety valve that may caution against some policy or action through the relationship between the monarch and the prime minister. This occurs in the realm of privacy and so one does not know how effective this is – it probably varies according to the persons involved. Such a ceremonial role, however, is needed for any advanced society and the majority of the UK population seem happy to accept this situation. In effect, the British are no longer subjects, but citizens of a country operating much like a republic. If we are so near to being a republic, why change? Of course, a number of Western democracies are republics and do not have monarchs. Others have monarchs, who are largely national figureheads.

The distinction between a subject and a citizen is, however, critical. A subject is required to act exactly as specified by a higher authority who has gained this position through privilege (ostensibly divine or through power).[216] Citizens too have to behave in certain ways prescribed by higher authority, but that authority is accountable to the citizens in the way it operates. Citizens have a responsibility to see that those in authority act appropriately. It was necessary to have mythical Gods, charismatic individuals as leaders of religion, monarchs and powerful overlords to direct the development of society. However, as the rank and file of people gained an understanding of how society should function, they wished to have a more prominent say in how that society was run. Hence, citizens should take a serious responsibility in choosing their leaders and policies.[217] This is now the essence of a democracy.

Philosophers recognised, however, that Man is competitive and needed a central authority to control his excesses and maintain order, but also to undertake analyses of problems and leadership in proposing and implementing solutions for them. In many situations this will require collaborate action from citizens or sections of society. Although citizens should hold their political leaders to account, those citizens also, in return, must accept some direction from the centre to benefit from collaborative action. One can see this theme right through from the Magna Carta. There has also been a thread running through political philosophy for some time about the competitiveness of man being enabled, not controlled, to provide the basis for inventiveness to further human progress. The Government should do what it can to enable this in a fair manner. There were, of course, experiments with totalitarian regimes like Communism and National Socialism. It will be noted, however, that these regimes did not provide freedom from false arrest and imprisonment (or worse). These totalitarian States persisted for some time, but now seem to have failed in the West.[218]

---

[216] The religious authorities seem to expect its followers to act as subjects.

[217] This is probably a simplification. Many still want to do nothing more than focus on their own needs and rights. Provided that these are not compromised too much, they do not seek any societal responsibility. If this is so, we have a nation of semi-subject-citizens.

[218] Of course, totalitarian forms of communism still persist in China and North Korea and extensive Government control still exists in Russia. Also, parts of the world have met difficulty when attempting to become modern democracies. The Arab Spring and postwar Iraq provide examples.

After their failure, the notion of the type of social collaboration needed changed and there was increased emphasis on taking care of those in need as well as planning for human advancement without going to totalitarian extremes. There was an increased emphasis on achieving a balance between justice and citizens' welfare.

So, in general, a Government should defend the realm and maintain fairness amongst its citizens by guaranteeing freedom from false arrest and imprisonment or unjustified seizing of property for its subjects/citizens, act in the wider benefit of its citizens and be held to account for its actions. From the perspective of early in the 21st century, these conclusions based on a quick review of a few key philosophers seem unremarkable and very general in nature. Nevertheless, these philosophers have come to be seen as giants in the field of political philosophy no doubt, in part, due to the influence they had at their time. Their conclusions, collectively, seem to set out the need for and general principles to be adopted by liberal democracies. It is interesting how the key concepts of identity, competition, fairness, collaboration, compassion and human pleasure, which have been central to my exploration of other areas of philosophy, have all come to the fore as factors underpinning modern democracy. The task now is to consider where this leaves us in the context of the year 2021 and how can this heritage be built upon? Moreover, as Kenny suggests, it will be seen that progress is likely to come from a fusion between political philosophy, politics, economics and sociology.[219]

Before going ahead, it is worth stating one caveat. While the governing system in democracies seems now to be well established and in little need

---

[219] It might be argued that political philosophy concerns seeking 'what ought to be' as universalities of social organisation whatever individual interests exist and that when one moves to examining individual policies, taking into account specific interests, the process becomes one of identifying 'what is' and this is political theory. I am arguing that one can seek to adopt a general process for strategic decision-making that ought to be used to formulate policies based upon the five factors listed in the previous Section whatever one's interests. That is different from specifying what the policies themselves, with specific interests and in specific circumstances, should be and so has, in my view, more of a philosophical tinge about it than just politics.

of further debate, recent developments suggest that one should not be complacent and simply assume these conditions will continue. There may always be the possibility of strong men or elites to gain control and want to retain it in whatever way they can.[220] If countries in the West want to maintain their democratic form, it must be kept under review. This is not a philosophical matter; the principles have been largely established, society needs a governing structure to ensure that they will be observed.

Current and Future Issues

Moving down (albeit only a little) from such broad generalisations, one may conceive of economic and other activity taking three forms, each reflecting a different ideology (identity) about what is needed to ensure effectiveness and ethical behaviour:

(1) where Government both organises and operationally runs activities within public ownership;
(2) where Government direction is applied to ensure that some other party or the market organises and acts appropriately;
(3) where Government leaves policy making, planning and operation totally to the market.

Usually Governments and political groups will have a fairly entrenched ideology of what blend of these three forms is required based largely on beliefs and experience which emerged over many years. Eastern nations such as China, North Korea and Russia will tend to opt for much more emphasis on (1) and (2) than Western countries like our own, Europe and the USA. Even within countries the mix between public and private sector will vary from time to time. For example, the Labour Party under leadership of Jeremy Corbyn threatened a very wide extension of public ownership if he became Prime Minister. In contrast, those on the right wing of the Tory Party seem to believe that as much economic activity as possible should

---

[220] The end of Trump's tenure as President of the USA comes to mind, but I doubt if he is unique.

be initiated, planned and operated in the private sector. As well as the size of the public sector, there is also the question of how resources should be allocated between competing demands within that sector and this will be subject to much political bargaining. Is it appropriate, however, for the size of the public sector and how it allocates resources between public services to be driven by broad ideologies? Ought not each public sector activity to be analysed to see what form of control and operation best suits its needs and then the outcome of those analyses used as the basis of the public sector size and resource allocation?

There will clearly be politics underlying such a process. Different political groups will have different views on the goals of each service and how best to achieve them efficiently while maintaining their own views on ethical standards. Also, crises, technological and other developments will arise from time to time which call for a rebalancing of resources and even a move to a larger or smaller public sector spend. The recent coronavirus crisis or the experience of war provides examples of when crises lead to a move back towards centralisation of control. The suggestion is, however, that the issue of the degree of central control, size of the public sector and how public sector resources are allocated should not be driven, semi-slavishly, by very broad political ideologies, but by being built up from what is needed to best achieve the aims of each type of service for the foreseeable future. The process should be more bottom up, rather than top down, even though, when analysing each service, views will be different about the degree of centrality over policy, planning and control that is required. This would provide a more flexible and responsive approach to determining the scale of Government control and activity allowing it to wax and wane, and even evolve, as circumstances change.

Political philosophers might look at the way the role of each public service is analysed. They do not have to decide on solutions to how money is spent, controlled or other practical problems and that is certainly not my objective here; that is the Parliament's and Government's role driven by political forces. However, political philosophers might consider how the main themes developed in Section 7, namely *Identity (including disposition towards Ethical practice and desire for Recreation), Competitive Environment,*

Empathy, Innovation and Collaboration, might be interpreted, considered and integrated in *each one* of these Government roles as set out in the list below and taken into account by decision makers. Of course, debates around these five themes already occur with regard to each public sector service, but it might be interesting to review how they might apply to each Government Department.

It might also be noted here that competitive environment needs to be considered at two levels for each department. First, does each Department have to compete in any sense with threats to its identity (this might be called competitive environment 1) and, second, to what extent should it employ the private sector to achieve its goals in a competitive manner within its service (to be called competitive environment 2)? The two may be related where the nature of the external threat influences how far a Government relies on collaboration with the private sector, but they should be considered separately.

Also such extensive strategic analysis like that proposed does not need to be taken every year, unless unexpected crises demand it. Years ago, companies were often urged to adopt zero-based budgeting where the need for every single item in their budgets was questioned. This usually proved to be impractical and too time consuming. Some organisations then adopted a process called 'sunset budgeting' whereby different sections of the budget were zero-based every few years. A similar approach could be used for periodic strategic reviews of the different Government roles, although a more comprehensive review might be needed in order to respond to a crisis.

The following lists six main areas of Government responsibilities to be considered and tries to illustrate where the five different factors developed in Section 7 might apply and need periodic review.

KEY GOVERNMENT ROLES
Defence of the realm
Health and social care (including housing)
Education and training
Environmental matters
Promotion of trade and economic growth (including the Treasury and taxation)
Citizen's general welfare

Defence

Defence needs to be considered in two parts. First, it is necessary for the Government to identify threats and make preparations to deal with them if they occur. Second, it will on occasion need to take action to respond to attacks. The main threats are internal insurrection, external military attacks, terrorist attacks, industrial espionage, cyberattacks and, more recently, space weapons which might destroy satellites. The cost of such threats succeeding is likely to be so severe that there may be little call for compassion in framing the direct defences and responses to them, although, in trying to respond to these threats, a consideration should be given to protecting innocent people even if, in extreme cases, such consideration is overruled. There are also some ethical considerations even in conducting war such as non-use of poison gas as a weapon. Similarly, fairness and recreation will be very secondary considerations. Even so, threats can be of varying likelihood and so there will always be a trade-off between organising defence and any undesirable impact on citizens. Very clearly the Government must be concerned with its Defence Department's competitive environment 1; it the very essence of what this Department is for.

How the Government monitors such threats and plans to deal with them may well require a considerable degree of private sector collaboration or even collaboration with other nations. The involvement of the private sector might also be through competitive contracting (competitive environment 2). It may also be necessary to call upon increased public awareness and collaboration to identify threats and the precise identity of those providing such threats. A careful analysis of the type and source of threat is clearly required to act competitively against it. This will require acquiring an empathy of rivals to understand exactly what they are trying to achieve and likely to do. Also, if threats develop such that physical response is necessary, even greater cooperation from private sector companies and the public will be usually be required, even in the form of joining the Government's armed forces.

The central issues for debate on defence are, therefore, how does the Government go about identifying major threats and the identity of those doing the threatening? What degree of competition (in competitive environment

1) is needed to counteract those threats? What degree and type of innovation is required to cope with each specific threat? What mix of public and private activity (competitive environment 2) is needed to identify and to prepare to cope with them? What scale of advance preparedness and reaction is needed and what circumstances make that necessary? This will involve a sensitive understanding of national and threatening group identities in an attempt to predict behaviour. It will also require an understanding of what is needed to compete militarily and technologically and what degree of collaboration, and with whom, it is needed. Also, despite fairness being a secondary matter where major threats are concerned, it may also be important to consider fairness where there are members of apparently threatening groups which do not offer threats themselves. For example, with a multi-ethnic society, the Government must be wary of acting unfairly towards innocent members of ethnic groups and penalising them unjustly, especially when dealing with possible terrorist attacks. If it does not, it may actually create further threats or make them more difficult to handle. This indicates that the identity of the source of the threat must be very carefully identified and not just taken to be a broad ethnic grouping. There will need to be fairness too in sharing contracting risks with private sector companies if good collaboration is to be achieved.

The need for a careful analysis of identities, competitive strength, ethics, the need for innovation and collaboration is clearly necessary to formulate defence policy and operations. Recreation would not seem to figure obviously, unless one includes not putting troops under pressure for too long and taking that into account in designing operating practices. Nothing really new has been proposed here. Debates based on the five factors specified are obviously considered now and major Defence Reviews are periodically undertaken. Moreover, quite appropriately for defence, they must often be held beyond the public gaze, but it will always be beneficial to reappraise the current review practice to consider whether it is rigorous enough or need updating.

The last few paragraphs assumed that the nation had a clear unvarying identity. History has shown that it does not. National borders have often been modified as a consequence of wars and other developments like Brexit and possible Scottish Independence. A change in national identity like this clearly has defence implications, but the issues involved in these recent boundary shifts extend far wider than this and will be dealt with later under Citizen's General Welfare.

Health

In the UK a long-standing debate has addressed the National Health Service. Should it be absolute, providing free care for everyone? Or should it be means tested? Or even, free for some elements of health care, but not for others? Or, indeed, should the whole system be privatised? The NHS has now been in existence since the 1940s, but still these issues are raised as, with growing numbers of older people and more advanced technology, the costs of that service threaten to become prohibitive. This, together with a threat of the service being totally unable to cope due to an unexpected pandemic, provides a clear competitive environment 1 to be analysed. A sense of compassion and fairness is relevant in addressing these questions. A central ethical issue involved is to what extent should the younger, working population be expected to provide ever increasing provision for the country's health system from taxation? Or whether the UK should move, at least partly, to an insurance-based system as employed in many other countries. In the past these questions have been settled (or pushed aside) mainly by political pressure and ideology (identity). Is it appropriate now to reassess these matters and the ideology on a rational basis and if so, how should this be conducted and what considerations should be involved?

This financing of the system is quite an independent issue from who should actually deliver health services in the country. Should it be totally state operated or to what extent should private sector health providers be incorporated into the system, perhaps competitively (competitive environment 2)? Whether it is to be run wholly by the State, in conjunction with private companies or totally by private sector providers, there is the issue of how it should be structured. Even if it is wholly owned by the State, should Government and the central health authority do little more than set the general parameters for allowable health care, and leave the forecasting of need, planning and operation to regional trusts or private bodies? It is sometimes argued that the latter would encourage innovation and a more ready response when needed.

This last argument is, at present, quite topical with the pandemic due to the coronavirus. The UK Government, in step with many other countries, has attempted to keep the spread of the virus under control. In retrospect, it has been criticised for being inadequately ready to meet such a crisis and employed tactics the effectiveness of which many have questioned. It has acted on scientific advice, but the science itself could not predict certain outcomes. So, in future, where should responsibility best lie for predicting and planning for possible pandemics? Would it be better left to local health service trusts to make their own plans? Or should it rest with a national health body? Whichever it is, how far should private sector companies be included in this system? Should they develop and control the virus testing centres and vaccine seeking activities? Experience with coronavirus has also shown that there was a learning process involved as the Government tried to cope with the crisis. How can one ensure in future that the learning process is, itself, organised and accountable? This applies, furthermore, to undertaking research in general on health issues. What combination of public/private activity should be employed on this? Can the private sector market be relied on to undertake necessary fundamental research as well as its search for required drug variations in its quest to earn profits? Can the market be relied upon to select the most appropriate mix of investigation between different diseases? How can the most appropriate mix be decided? All these issues show the need for debate about the place of competition and collaboration.

A further ethical issue has been highlighted by the coronavirus crisis. The Government decided that the economy and social activity had to go into lockdown (either nationally or on a local differentiated basis according to the severity of the virus infection in each region) in order to contain the spread of the virus. This raised the question of how far lockdown should go without infringing the rights of individuals to act freely and enjoy their recreation. As seems to be the case when any major catastrophe occurs, such as a major war or pandemic, the population is generally ready to act unselfishly as guided in order to act in the wider interests of society.

Indeed, this widespread collaboration is then often held up as a desirable norm for future social behaviour. Once the threat has considerably reduced or disappeared, there is, however, a tendency for most members of the population to be less willing to collaborate so widely at the expense of their own freedom of activity. Moreover, the consequence of lockdown is not just a question of individual rights, but of the potential collapse of the economy and the associated costs for health, education and personal well-being as well as international competition on trade. Empathy with those affected is needed to provide a good understanding of their positions and forecast how they are likely to react in terms of compliance with central directions and also express views subsequently in votes.

This raises the bigger issue, beyond the coronavirus case, of what is the role of Government? The decision on how much to allocate planning and action in response to a crisis to each of the private sector and public sector, is not the same as specifying to what extent should it protect citizens from the risks they face? While this dilemma arose quite clearly in the coronavirus case, it should be considered in relation to all services, although it relates especially to Health, Social Care, Education and Citizens' General Welfare. By implication it is already, by the assumption of certain powers by the Government (e.g. providing a National Health Service, subsidising Social Care or free Education) and by the practice of individuals taking out insurance cover for a large range of risks, but, when the coronavirus struck, it was not immediately clear what financial support the Government should give to those affected by lockdown. Is there the need for more precise rules to guide what risks citizens should accept as their own responsibility?

The Government has a very complex situation to manage involving a number of competing moralities and is clearly struggling with it at the time of writing this. Whatever, it decides, some will say that it has got it wrong. Can political philosophers offer a systematic way to address this problem? This is also linked closely with the need for central authorities to be accountable for their actions. How should accountability be framed when taking the correct decision is dominated by so much uncertainty? It seems natural to suggest that by making the decision process and information on which it is based as open as possible will help to provide a sensible assessment of accountability.

But how open should that be? In an uncertain world mistakes will be made. How can it be decided that any reasonable person in that situation would have made the same error? If that cannot be guaranteed, the decision-maker will be likely to conceal the decision process and, if possible, the mistakes. On the other hand, is it the threat of being held accountable for failure, even if the action taken was reasonable, the means by which society can be confident that every effort will be made to get things right? How can this be made consistent with the political process whereby the Opposition is expected to be confrontational and take advantage of any weakness in the Government's position.

Moreover, Governments are expected to treat its citizens fairly, but the population comprises varying groups with quite different identities and interests. Which identities should get priority on what? In order to address this issue, should an attempt be made publicly to mould and define these identities on the basis of common features? Or would that actually create more upheaval and dissension? It is very clear that strategic reviews of this service need to consider Identity, Competitive Environment, Empathy, Innovation and Recreation.

Social Care
Closely aligned with Health Issues is the matter of social care. To some extent this is a modern problem brought about by people moving to different parts of the country for work and living. 60 years ago and more, families tended to stay local and the younger members took care of their elders. In the vast majority of cases this no longer occurs giving rise to the need for a compassionate State having to care for those unable to care for themselves. This includes the provision of care homes and financial support for those incapacitated, but who can still manage to look after themselves at home – often with visiting or live-in help. Once more, the issue arises about means testing versus free provision of care. Should there be a limit set on the payment for care – even where the patient has a modest amount of capital? Apart from financing care, the issue of organisation arises as in general health care. Should the State provide for all care or leave most to the private sector to provide, expecting a system of insurance to be developed to

cover the costs?[221] Once again a consideration of the need for competition, collaboration, fairness and compassion underlies all these issues.

Housing

The provision of adequate housing has been an issue in the UK for some time. A competitive environment 1 may be seen to exist as simply a growing excess of demand over supply, including the desired distribution of housing regionally. The main problem currently is the provision of sufficient accommodation at an affordable rate for younger members of society. This situation has arisen through a combination of factors including policies over the availability of land, the growing size of population and social trends leading to many single parent families thereby requiring more accommodation in aggregate and, in some areas, immigration policies. But should the thrust for new housing be made on a more subtle basis than focusing on the provision of affordable mass accommodation for the young. Is there not a need for a careful assessment of the distribution of the population over different groups (identities) and where they will be employed as new industries or services develop, over the next, say, 50 years? Housing policy along these lines might provide a balanced supply of housing. Of course, such population forecasting takes place now by the Government and private construction companies. But how effective has it been, if there is now such a dearth of affordable property? Do the prediction models need to be improved?

Practically all new housing is provided by the private sector, whereas after the Second World War much was provided by public authorities. The current coronavirus lockdown has meant that house building has virtually stopped. Will it get going again as quickly as desirable? Is there a case for a, albeit temporary, return to some public sector building after a major crisis? Perhaps not, but can public and private sector collaboration be improved to

---

[221] Some would say that NIC was initially intended to be an approximation to this, but it is now seen by Government as just another tax levy to go into the general pot of resources. It is not earmarked for health and care and each individual's contribution is not related to the amount of care he/she gets or has to pay for.

rectify this situation – either by release of more land by planning authorities, rules to force companies to release land they currently hold, or financial help or risk avoidance schemes for both specific groups of house purchasers and builders? Is there a need for innovation in building, such as factory or 3d printing construction or changes in work practices? Should tax be increased to fund or subsidise such initiatives? The usual ethical issue arises when any proposal involves an increase in tax for those not benefiting from the initiative.

Competing ethical stances are involved. How much green land should be freed for building houses? Recent suggestions to change planning procedures have divided land into three types: 1. open for building without planning permission, 2. open but subject to permission and 3. completely protected against building. Where should the dividing lines between these three categories be drawn? If planning is relaxed, will one get urban sprawl like much of that in the USA and Continental Europe? Does that matter and to whom (i.e. to what identities)? To what extent should aesthetics and recreation play a part in controlling new build?

Education and training

It is very clear at the outset of considering this service that there is a severe external threat to the whole system at present as a result of the coronavirus pandemic (competitive environment 1). Universities, colleges and schools have had to limit their operations with the education of students and pupils suffering as a result. The identity of the threat is obvious, but it calls into question what the identity education itself should be in future if it is to insulate itself against such threats. The recent move to online instruction be improved and might become more permanent or, perhaps, the construction of educational buildings which are capable of being turned rapidly into better protection against pandemics. The education system has also to be fit for purpose to compete against threats to its ability to allow the country to compete internationally in both commerce and defence.

Following the Second World War the Labour Government took steps to widen education for all. Secondary education was made available to all and grammar school education available to those who pass the entrance exams.

This was continued with free university education for those who could gain entrance. Now, however, university students are expected to pay sizeable fees for their courses. This, combined with encouragement of universities to take in much larger numbers of students, has meant that many who would not have qualified for entrance a number of years ago have been admitted. Some would suggest that this in turn has led to a downgrading of degrees awarded by some institutions. This calls for a careful analysis of the quality of degrees by businesses and others using them as a guide for recruiting employees. On the other hand, if many more are getting a higher education because of this, perhaps this is a very welcome trend socially and economically.

While secondary education is still available for all without payment of fee, grammar schools have largely been closed down, mainly, on the basis that they reinforced class distinction and were unfair to those unable to attend them who, it was often claimed, were in such a situation because of their more deprived background which did not encourage or facilitate study.[222] These changes obviously had the political intention to improve productivity and international competitiveness, but they were also driven by a concern for fairness and compassion. On the other hand, these changes might have reduced competition both for places in higher education and within it. So, the issues are similar to those in health. Should education be universally free? Should it be free at some basic level, but not higher levels? Are recruiting processes fair amongst different social classes and ethnic groups? Should there be a more competitive process to gain higher levels of education?

The design of the teaching curriculum might also be subject to debate. Should there be a national syllabus for all to follow? If so, should this be comprehensive or at just a national minimum? Or should there be none at all allowing educational institutions to develop their own approaches, possibly also then being free to recruit as many as they like if their programmes are more attractive to the public? This applies at all levels of education.

---

[222] When grammar schools existed, some children from very poor backgrounds were able to get some financial support even for them to attend grammar school, though this was the exception rather than the norm.

For example, should the university system be required to focus mainly on meeting the nation's expected needs for subjects such as technology? Or, if the universities do not make adequate provision for those needs, can it be left to in-company degree level educational innovations like those introduced by Dyson to fill the gap?

In education too, the role and influence of trade unions is significant. Are schools and educational institutions run too much for the providers and not enough for the pupils or, indeed, to meet the requirement of employers or international competition? This further raises a similar question for universities on the relationship between research and teaching. Do academics place more emphasis on their research and less to teaching? Is teaching better at top research universities? Are top research institutes more interested in discovering and developing those of their students that will make good researchers? The reference to none of these questions is meant to imply that some actions are desirable and some are not. But they need to be argued out properly, recognising identities, competition, fairness and, in a minority of cases, compassion.

As stated above, coronavirus has had a major impact on universities. While public funded schools may be expected to survive the crisis, universities are independent bodies expected to balance their own financial books. The Government provides financial support for both teaching and research, but students now pay fees and universities are, at present, allowed to recruit any number of students they like, including foreign students who pay higher fees.[223] The coronavirus crisis has meant that, until it is past, there will be fewer foreign students and many UK would-be students are thinking of deferring their higher education as many universities decide only to provide all lectures online. This places a number of universities with the prospect of large financial deficits and perhaps little prospect of regaining a positive financial position if student numbers do not return to previous levels after the virus threat has ceased.

A response suggested by some politicians has been to reduce the number of universities, particularly those thought to be offering lower standard

---

[223] There is currently some political debate about changing this.

degrees. This would, of course, raise again the initial ethical debate about the percentage of the population that should benefit from higher education. If, however, there were a transformation of those universities offering lower standard degrees into more technically based institutions (modern versions of the previous Colleges of Technology), the percentage of the population gaining from higher education could be maintained and their education made more relevant to future employment and national competitiveness. This form of education might be in collaboration with business and the provision of apprenticeships. Another consequence may be that the traditional role of an academic as both a teacher and researcher will be changed, with people appointed to do one or the other. To cut costs many casual employees used to support teaching may no longer be employed and new curricula developed suitable for online teaching. This will place a considerable burden on current full-time academic staff such that many more may have to specialise in teaching alone. Researchers will then be almost wholly employed on funded projects, but, as is discussed below when considering innovation, will this mean that a lot of original ideas from a more widespread and diverse academic faculty will be lost? Also research ideas do come from time to time from teaching.

A solution might be for universities to reformulate how higher education might be delivered. This might even be done by the Government introducing a national online lecture package for, say, first- and second-year undergraduates. Indeed these first two years might be taken at home and attendance at university and contact with academics taking two years at university after that. This might enable a marked reduction of costs for both universities and students. There is also the question of whether more private sector universities should be introduced in the UK (competitive environment 2). The UK has the University of Buckingham, but the USA has many private universities. Michael Crow, President of Arizona University, has recently called for a much more extensive review of how the US university system should be run. As well as using technology to improve the teaching process, he has suggested that the university system should be looked at as a whole. It is not just a question of improving what individual universities do, but of improving the whole sector. This might well include more cooperation between universities on both teaching and research. Different universities have different strengths, why not have more cross university teaching and research? Many universities in the UK will say there is already much cooperation, at least on research. There is also the question of whether students get a better total experience at university if they mix with those from different disciplines.

These are just possible concerns currently being discussed. I stress that I am not proposing any particular stance on them nor am I suggesting that philosophers determine the solutions. Rather that they should be aware of the sort of solutions that might be offered and explore their philosophical dimensions in terms of the general themes of what is needed in terms of identity,[224] competitive strengths internationally and the development of a civilised society supported by appropriate collaboration and innovation. This applies right across the system from preschool, primary school, secondary school, university education at both undergraduate and postgraduate and research levels.

Environmental matters

Concern for the environment has gained more publicity in recent years such that it is now a major Governmental consideration. Of course, the Government has always addressed environmental issues. Large strides have been made to cleanse rivers and canals and organise collection of refuse and other forms of waste. It seems that responsibility for general cleansing is well established and does not need further debate about collaboration, although, perhaps, the divide between local authority and private company services might be revisited, together with the role individuals should play in this process. However, there is a major problem in how to cope with the growth of plastic disposals on Earth and a growing concern about rubbish circulating in space. New collaborative action is required here at international level. The dominant issue gaining attention at present is, however, global warming and what form of fuel we should use for transport

---

[224] What exactly different sections of the educational system are for and how to designate them so that this is clear.

to heat our homes as well as for industrial use.

Several years ago the emphasis was mainly on pollution and the UK Government introduced incentives, first, to move to diesel cars and then away from them. In more recent years there has been an increased emphasis on fears attached to global warming and this has led to calls for more transport and other energy needs to be met by electricity or hydrogen. Governments in many countries are trying to limit reliance on fossil fuels and rely more upon power derived from solar, water or plant sources. As part of this effort Governments provide incentives for saving energy and adopting sources which have reduced or zero emissions. In the UK, the Government has issued declarations saying a move to electric vehicles will become mandatory for new cars from a prescribed date. One suspects, however, that it will take far more than changing cars to conquer this problem. It is something that all individuals, public authorities, companies and other businesses will need to address in order to see what each can contribute.

At first, there hardly seems to be a philosophical issue to be addressed here. It seems obvious that if nothing is changed and global warming predictions were met, the cost would be so severe that action must be taken now. It also seems obvious, however, that a really significant step forward in reduction of global warming will only be made if nations, especially all developed ones, act in unison. This presents a major problem in collaboration, both between different economic entities and countries. There is a gleam of hope. Not long ago the ozone layer was severely holed, but, after global action, it is now recovering. Hence, international cooperation can be achieved where vital, but not without inter-Governmental effort.

Issues relating to fairness and compassion are also involved. If global warming continues, one might expect regional weather patterns to change with some countries, probably the less developed nations, experiencing droughts and hardship with which they are not well able to cope. Developing countries also argue that they still have to achieve their industrialisation and, hence, should be allowed to use readily available fossil fuels to achieve that. This raises a major international ethical issue.

The need for climate change also places a direct responsibility on manufacturers as well as land, sea and air transporters to develop innovative products and practices to reduce their carbon emissions.

It follows that philosophical issues do arise over environmental matters with respect to international collaboration, fairness and even some sense of compassion for some less developed countries. It is also obvious that considerable effort at innovation and collaboration, between and within countries, will be needed to solve these problems.

Promotion of trade and economic growth

Trade and growth has always been a key role of Government. Even several hundred years ago when Governmental management was less extensive, there was encouragement from kings and the elite classes to search out profitable activities around the world. Although methods of competition have changed somewhat from practices used in the past,[225] it is still vitally important for a country to remain internationally competitive if it wishes to maintain the standard of living of its citizens. The Government therefore frames policies to help and encourage private sector businesses to compete.

The economic stimulation has, very recently, become centre stage in politics due to the action taken in response to coronavirus. Billions of pounds have been spent in the UK on furlough and other payments to people thrown out of work by the social lockdown, and in subsidies and grants to businesses. These payments had a multiple role: to help those deprived of their income sources, and thereby encourage them to comply with lockdown rules, and also to try to maintain aggregate demand at an acceptable level. The Government now has a major task to help the economy come out of lockdown and return to economic growth as soon as possible. Without that unemployment and welfare payments will rise considerably. At the same time taxes may need to be increased and other public sector expenditure squeezed in order to repay the large debt run up by the Government. Without an early return to growth and reduction in unemployment, much hardship will be experienced. The Government (and just about everyone else) is very clearly aware of this and there are signs that it intends to stimulate growth by increased expenditure on major

---

[225] Slavery, seizing wealth and property, taking over native communities, etc. come to mind.

projects and incentives. It is also recognised that while some argue that the Government accumulating a much larger debt does not matter too much because of very low interest rates, others say this may not last and that increased taxation will be needed to repay this debt. As soon as increased or new taxes are proposed, there are obvious questions of competition, fairness and compassion to be considered.

A central part of government is the management of *The Treasury and Taxation* with its impact on all of the Government services mentioned. In political debates the Treasury viewpoint often dominates because all other Government Departments need finance to conduct their operations. The Treasury, along with the Bank of England, also plays a part in determining the level of economic activity. As already stated, major contributions have been made by the Treasury in 2020 to give furlough support for those who would otherwise be unemployed due to the coronavirus. It has also given massive support to businesses and other organisations in the way of grants and loans. Simultaneously, the Bank of England has increased the money supply and reduced interest rates to nearly zero which supports the stock market and aims to encourage borrowing to invest and create the conditions for growth. The Treasury and Chancellor of the Exchequer also determine what type and level of taxes to levy and, by implication, what level of debt the country can carry. To some extent, the concept of identity plays a part in this process. Is this a country that tries to balance revenue against expenditure taking one year with another (e.g. as Germany did) or is it comfortable with deficit financing and borrowing on a long-term basis? Is this country one that believes in regressive taxes? To what extent does fairness and even compassion determine decisions? Are the effects on different identities always assessed? How should funds be allocated between departments even if a thorough analysis of how to run them individually has been undertaken? Is it necessary, where there is less competitive pressure, to impose financial pressure on departments to impose more discipline to look for improvements?

After their recent election victory, the Tories acknowledged that there was unfairness in the way wealth and income was spread around the country. They promised to move towards a more equal distribution of wealth between regions of the UK. The coronavirus pandemic diverted attention from this, but when that issue wanes the UK Government will, presumably, begin to readdress its promises to make an effort to rectify the inequalities. Apart from the mechanics of how to do this, there is the question of what degree of unfairness exists and exactly where, how is it to be measured and what are the consequences, what caused it to arise and how does knowledge of these reasons enable an improvement to be made? Is it really just a matter of large projects giving increased employment for their duration, important though that might be?

In some areas, the requirements to stimulate growth can only be achieved by Government action. The development of national road and transport systems is an obvious example. Government action alone will not, however, give the country sufficient competitiveness or growth. Government policies and encouragement play a part, but the essential task will fall to the private sector. The question of what lasting effect the virus crisis had had on business confidence and practice will need to be considered. This crisis has revealed how exposed some businesses are in being tied in to just-in-time practices and foreign supply chains. These practices were encouraged from about 20 years ago to gain further gains from the Law of Comparative Advantage and operate more efficiently. Yet, if such supply chains are disrupted, businesses cannot continue to gain these advantages. Will this crisis lead companies to pull more of their supply chains back into the UK to ensure continued delivery? Will this uncertainty lead to the need to rebalance the UK economy by reintroducing more manufacturing of vital goods and not rely so much on services and software production? If so, will this affect competitiveness and wealth creation? Moreover, will companies become more risk averse having just faced damaging losses and, in some cases, complete corporate collapse from being too highly geared financially to withstand the drop in sales activity? If so, they may not be so keen to return to large scale investment for a time. Added to the problem may be the reaction of consumers, who also having faced financial hardship, recognise the need for greater savings to provide a buffer against hard times. That might well lead to even more downward pressure on some businesses, although the banks could play some part in reducing this effect by spending the increased savings deposits and worthwhile investment. Clearly the pursuit of competition in the changed environment will be central to this situation and underlying all progress to a competitive position is innovation. There is, hence, the need for a more widespread debate and recognition of how to generate innovation – and innovation in the appropriate areas.

What should be the Government's role in furthering innovation? Innovation can be achieved in different ways and at different levels. For success in some areas, large scale, fundamental research is needed. The UK Government's recent proposal to establish key research institutes in each region is a move both to help equalise regional wealth, but also to improve competitiveness in the UK. Where major national issues are involved, such as in Defence matters, the Government also needs to play a key role. That does not mean that all such research must be conducted in publicly owned bodies. The Government needs to provide an oversight, direction and incentives for it to be done effectively. Clearly, issues arise of what forms of collaboration should take place and with what types of organisations for different types of research and development. Also, how should the rewards for success or costs of failure be fairly distributed? With matters of national significance, consideration must also be given to the extent that reliance may be made on foreign sources of help. There may be a straight contradiction between keeping the nation's defence and industrial secrets safe and the need to gain improved productivity through specialisation across nations and the Law of Comparative Advantage. This is not just an economic issue. Economic, political and social consequences of alternative actions need to be explored.

By far the majority of innovation takes place beyond Government direction. As stated already, at all levels of society a competitive position can usually be maintained only by continually seeking to innovate. There is always either someone else seeking to outcompete the firm currently in top position or there is an environmental change that means that current methods are no longer so successful. Each individual business, large or small, must spend time considering how meaningful innovation can be achieved within its type of activity and how it can differentiate itself from rivals. This can, of course, be sought in differences in source of supply, energy or manpower, production processes and product characteristics, distribution networks, advertising or services offered, including post-sale servicing. So much is fairly obvious. The key point question for the Government is how can this innovation be stimulated?

In two very recent, but quite separate, books, Wagner[226] and Ridley[227] put forward very similar arguments. Wagner argues that innovation is the centre of evolution and existed even before life began. By this he means there were new chemical reactions taking place long before some such reaction created the first form of life. As discussed earlier, in the Section dealing with the evolution of physical species, he argues that a considerable part of evolution is due to Recombination. That is the repeated association and mixing of different gene packages through populations. He then extends this logic to say that as evolution through innovation is ubiquitous, it also must apply to innovation in human activities, including new developments in technology, business, etc. By this he means essentially that innovation can be achieved by encouraging diversity across teams of problem solvers to provide a cross-fertilisation of ideas together with the freedom to experiment, going through a series of failures if necessary to achieve improvement. He stresses that what often appear to be 'eureka moments' are mostly the result of much earlier thinking and trial and error before the key breakthrough occurs.

Ridley acknowledges the contribution from Wagner, but also offers many useful case studies of innovations and how they arose. He shows that very few were centrally planned, either by the State or large corporation, and most arose from a long process of curious investigation by either individuals or small teams of people pursuing an idea. Often the breakthroughs came from unexpected sources such as ideas from different disciplines or chance observations. Ridley also emphasises the need from freedom of thought, action and the need for trial and error. Apart from a few major issues of national importance, he says that the State should not interfere in such processes, although there were one or two acts it might take to encourage an environment conducive to innovation.

---

[226] Wagner, *Life Finds a Way*, op cit.
[227] M Ridley, *How Innovation Works*, 4th Estate, 2020.

As does Wagner, Ridley says that laws on bankruptcy could be modified to encourage innovation and tolerate failure in the trial and error process. Some US States, for example, allow owners of firms that have gone into liquidation to retain their homes. Patent and copyright laws are, in his view, too protective and unnecessary to stimulate innovation. Ripley continues to list a series of resistances to innovation that should be rectified. He illustrates the long battles waged against the introduction of coffee in a number of different countries and show that the resistance was due to a mixture of self-interest, vested interests and competitive paranoia. He likens to the actions taken against coffee, the steps to control genetically modified crops and foods. He also quotes the fears generated against products like the weedkiller (Roundup) which ignore the science behind the product. He says that Roundup has transformed agriculture allowing the control of weeds by chemical means, obviating ploughing. He accuses bounty-hunting law firms searching the next tobacco-sized windfall. Such activism is a significant deterrent to innovation. He also quotes the story of mobile phones as one in which Government resisted innovation in league with vested interests of the private sector. He also states that, in the so-called interests of competition, powerful corporate bodies can influence Government in ways which reduce innovation. He reproduces an insightful reference to William Baumol, the economist, which captures very clearly what he means. Baumol says that, if the best way to get rich is to build a new device and sell it, entrepreneurs will innovate, but, if it is simpler to lobby Government to set up rules in favour of their existing technology, the entrepreneurs will focus on lobbying and not innovation. Finally, he suggests making much greater use of awarding prizes for new developments or Governments buying out patents, especially any patents that limit advancement in seeking other new developments.

In reviewing the part that Government should play in stimulating business growth, it seems we should distinguish between the short-run and the long-run. In the short-run, the Government does need to 'interfere' to cope with crises. There may need to be innovation, such as the development of a new vaccine to counter coronavirus. This may need the Government to encourage a diversity of approaches as well as exploring other means of, at least, alleviating the effect of the disease pending the identification of a new reliable vaccine. However, there is clearly innovative action that Government must take to support the general and business community during the first stages of the crisis. Even then, however, the Government needs to be careful not to be too protective. We have seen various innovative steps taken during the coronavirus crisis. Shopping online has been greatly extended such that there may, in future, be a much lower attendance at supermarkets themselves. If this occurs, there may well be scope for innovation by local suppliers, especially of fresh produce like vegetables. At the outset of the crisis, a small local greengrocer that we use responded to his shop closure by taking phone orders and employing a same-day delivery service. His business has expanded several-fold and will be continued now the shop is open again. Similarly, various local restaurants have organised takeaway or home delivery services which may endure as new lines of trade. Firms are also beginning to see that it is unnecessary to have all staff situated in a central office and much more working from home will probably continue to a considerable extent once the virus threat has died down. It should not be the Government's intention to change such innovations. In addition, the crisis may have simply brought forward a financial crisis in a firm that was heading for liquidation anyway. It is not the Government's role to prop up failing businesses, unless, perhaps, important security matters are involved. A Government has to act to prevent a major catastrophe, but it should try to balance that need with the avoidance of hindering new innovations.

It is in the longer-run, that the messages from Wagner and Ridley need to be taken on board. Their suggestions for encouraging a more innovative business environment are appropriate, but one gets the feeling that much more than that could be done. But what? Clearly solutions must involve rewards for those making significant inventions and scope for individual satisfaction where private motivation and curiosity is the main driver of enquiry. There is certainly the need to some high powered and clear thinking on the matter. Is that not what philosophers are good at? There is some evidence that this is beginning with the recent (August, 2020) suggestion to put entrepreneurs at the head of public sector bodies and give them more freedom of action. This may be one way forward, but, because the activity is in the public sector, this may indicate that the country cannot afford to have it make serious errors. In which case can there be quite the freedom to experiment and fail as Ripley and Wagner suggest? There can be if experiments are cordoned off and conducted in a way that does not affect the whole organisation if they fail.

As a final point on business stimulus, new inventions may be made, but there needs to be subsequent development to gain advantage from them. Often we hear of inventions being made in the UK, but development then taken up abroad. The Government probably has a role to play here by identifying and noting down the rate of progress of innovation in many different fields and ensuring that development is followed up as soon as appropriate. One might argue that private business does not need this and will proceed with development in order to be competitive. In which case, there needs to be a study of which inventions were not taken up in the UK, but taken up abroad, who did the inventing and with what motivation. Does this occur according to the type of activity/people giving rise to the invention? Does this occur where invention is more the result of individualistic motivation that need not be financial at all? Is this an important phenomenon or not?

Citizens' general welfare
The Government also has the responsibility to look after the general welfare of its citizens. The previous paragraphs on defence, health, environmental matters and trade are obviously all part of that process. Citizens need to feel safe in their country and its way of life, have reliable contract law and fair treatment in law, have access to good health care, have a clean environment and a reasonable assurance of a satisfactory standard of living. The points made earlier about unfairness in treatment of specific, though often large groups, are also very relevant to the nation's welfare and state of ease. The most obvious is creation of fairness for black and ethnic groups so that they identify with their own history and background, but also extend their perceived identity to consider themselves an integral part of the UK itself, willing to contribute to it and recognising that there are claims to be made by other identities with whom peaceable agreements need to be made. To be valuable concepts, identities often need to be seen as multilayered as

mentioned earlier.[228] The same applies to a lesser extent to regions of the UK.

In making progress with the problems of racial groups and regional inequality, it will be important to consider the group identities very carefully. Clearly there are inequalities, but it often seems that the group identity is portrayed as very general and inclusive and ignores more subtle variations amongst that group's members. For example, often very general declarations are made about lower wealth and opportunity of some ethnic groups. When it can be shown that, in the UK, ethnic groups, such as those of Chinese or Indian extraction, earn on average more than white people. Black people, apparently, only earn 9 per cent less on average. Of course, these are only averages. The downside tails of the distribution of black earnings could stretch much further to the left than for white people. There may be more poor black people counterbalanced by more who are better off. In terms of opportunity to improve their position, the worst achievers at getting into university in the UK are white people. Only 30 per cent of white applicants get accepted.[229] There is also considerable underachievement by poor white boys – not because of lack of opportunity, but, as Nelson[230] argues, because they consider that it is not worth trying to improve. In other words they have a limited identity of themselves and what they can achieve due to the environment in which they are growing up. General identities as portrayed in mass demonstrations and used to suggest that all black people or members of other subgroups are disadvantaged, need to be unpicked carefully.[231]

---

[228] Many members of the English soccer team are not white. Yet they consider themselves English while still most are proud of their black or other ethnic background.

[229] F Nelson, *The Telegraph*, 12 June, 2020.

[230] Nelson, op cit.

[231] There are other ways in which they need to be unpicked. There is the suggestion that riots are encouraged, even initiated, by groups wishing to create political upheaval for its own sake. Also some attending rallies seem to suggest they do it for the devil of it. Unfortunately, such participants, if viewed as such by a wider public, may create resistance to change and make it more difficult to remove social injustice and inequalities. In addition, excessive focus on the ethnic group identity and the history of slavery or colonisation may also imbed in the youth in that group the idea that all white men want to take advantage of them and are not to

Hillary Clinton once said that all demonstrations are attempting to create an identity. BAME has formed an identity to encompass black, Asian and minority ethnic people. Of course, where there are important issues affecting all members of BAME that is appropriate and forming a larger identity certainly helps to gain attention. However, as Nelson's statistics above illustrate, solutions may need to be different for different sub-identities. Do all members of BAME, for example, experience the same treatment by the police (especially in the USA) as the black people? Are other minor ethnic members really seeking something else? If black people that are poor suffer most, is it mainly because they are poor? If so, should a solution be sought by placing focus on improving conditions for the poor, including black, white and any other poor members of society? Exactly where does improvement need to be provided for black people and other ethnic groups? Exactly what is the nature and dimensions of the inequality? Exactly where is regional inequality in the UK to be removed and how? Using broad identities may be useful to get attention, but a more precise understanding of identities is needed to provide solutions. Efforts to rectify these inequalities must not be guided only by demonstrations, placards and statements of widespread unfairness relating to broad groups that are not really single identities at all, even though such declarations are quite legitimate and helpful in focusing attention where needed.

Similar arguments apply to consideration of the place of women in society. Just over 100 years ago, women demonstrated vigorously in a way similar to that being made by black people now. To a large extent, women have achieved what they were searching for, but, as recently as

---

be trusted, even though they may grow up in relatively good UK conditions. This may mean that it will take longer to bring about collaboration between white and ethnic groups to get rid of inequalities. Finally, there is the question of removal of statues and names associated with past famous men because of their links with the slave trade or colonisation. Obviously, one must not forget history and the lessons of the past. It is probably better to retain such public images, or at least, place them in properly organised museums with accurate details of their notable achievements shown alongside their nefarious activities, rather than let them disappear completely. If the latter happens, where is the history? Resolution of these matters will be difficult and will need understanding and collaboration by both sides.

the 1990s, there were sizeable demonstrations, especially in the USA, to further women's rights. It is still regularly claimed that there are disparities between the position of men and women which need examination. Again, to remove these inequalities properly, one needs to identify the precise scale and dimensions of the problem and what causes it.

The question of identity is also central to another current main issue; that of Brexit. The country was almost divided in two; one half wanting to leave the European Union and the other half wanting to stay in it. The Conservative Government, but by no means all of its members, clearly saw it as being in UK citizens' general interest to come out of the EU. These 'Leavers' foresaw both economic benefits in the longer run and emphasised the need for the UK to regain full control over its money, business, legal and parliamentary process. It presented a clear identity of the UK as not part of an increasingly federalised EU. The 'Remainers', in contrast, supported a clear identity of being part of the EU at the expense of reduced UK independence. They also emphasised that the costs of reverting to more independence now would be too high. As we now know, the 'Leavers' persuaded the majority of UK voters to support them and we await developments. The point here is that, in my view, the argument was so severe because the very identity of the UK was in question rather than due to economic considerations considerable though these are. The majority of UK citizens took the view that their own long established group identity as an independent country[232] was waning and they wanted to resist that. This also far outweighed traditional political allegiances and political parties that were divided between 'Leavers' and 'Remainers'. The current Government consists of a core of 'Leavers' and believes that it acted in the interests of the UK citizens' general welfare, but the event illustrates well the importance of identity at all levels in understanding behaviour.

The same sort of analysis can be applied to the question of Scottish Independence. The SNP wishes to establish a clear Scottish identity for the Scots with the declaration that Scots wish to run their own affairs. The UK

---

[232] Possibly imbedded by experience of two World Wars. Times have changed, but core identities can run deep and persist over long stretches of time.

Government wishes to maintain the identity of a unified UK. The eventual outcome will depend on political power, but that will in turn depend on who is best at establishing the preferred identity in the minds of its citizens.

Government responsibility does, however, extend to a more individual level than discussed above, although, perhaps, less importantly so in times of economic stress. Aesthetics are now a requisite feature of civilised societies. Using the broad interpretation of such a term, as used in the previous Section of this text, Government should exert effort to see that activities like art, sculpture, museums, music, theatre, cinema, writing books all prosper to provide cultural satisfaction of its citizens. To some extent these activities may be supported by Government grants where a very desirable activity is threatened and, where public sector provision is required, often supplied by local government. Less wealthy persons might benefit from some of these aesthetic activities and might be aided to partake in them though appreciation classes or general education or through public sector provision or financial discounts. But the private sector clearly plays a major part and many people are prepared to pay for such services. Where these activities can stand on their own feet, they probably should do so. People should be primarily responsible for their own amusement and satisfaction and most will certainly wish to do so.

At the end of the Section of this text on aesthetics, there was also a brief reference to the general search for pleasure and recreation. Obviously the Government would like to have a happy community of citizens. In fact, it is important to bear in mind that, to many people, the main purpose of their lives at work is to provide the means and time for pleasure whatever form that make take. Where this is removed, the population or sections of it can frustrate Government or other community action. An example is the recent invasion of beaches in summer, breaching social distancing advice, and possibly threatening a surge in coronavirus. It was as if many thought that 'this is what we do'. On a hot sunny day we go to the beach irrespective of what the Government might say. Similarly, if other pressures are brought to impinge upon leisure time, this may be reflected in the ballot box.

Conclusions on Political Philosophy

This previous paragraphs suggest that there is some advantage to be gained by reviewing separately each of the Government's main activities and roles by reference to the concepts of Identity (including ethical disposition and recreational needs), Competitive Environment, Empathy, Innovation and Collaboration. These concepts emerge from a general review of philosophy as fundamentally important to the operation of civilised society. By analysing *each* Government role by reference to these terms, it should be possible to gain insight into how each activity should be organised. What identities need to be satisfied by each government activity? How much competition should there be and where should it be located and focused? How much collaboration should there be between the public and private sectors to achieve success both in competition and in delivering required outcomes from public policies? What should be the size of the public sector? Where does fairness need to be improved between different identities and how can it be accomplished? How is compassion observed in Government policies and how is it to be supported throughout society and, given that there will be so many demands for special treatment, where are the priorities for action? These are all issues that, in my opinion, could be clarified by careful debate by philosophers and, thereby, enable politicians to make better decisions on actions to adopt.

The previous paragraph may give the impression that it is possible to have a completely rational system with most outcomes foreseeable and the best distribution of policy, planning and execution knowable. This is definitely not intended. A large and complex State has so many issues to face that it will be impossible to have full information of activities, outcomes and their link with effectiveness. As a consequence, there will be politics, by which I mean that there will be differences of views on the best location of these aspects of activities within society. This gives rise to different identities trying to get their view established as the main criterion for determining what happens. Also, because of this complexity, there will always be varying perceptions (sub-identities) of what is needed within each political group or party. The role of political parties is to form a group with sufficient consensus of what is most needed and gain power to implement it. The population cannot have a referendum on every major issue. Different political parties offer alternative menus in order to simplify voter choice.

As became clear from the review of political philosophy, eventually Western democracies arrived at some degree of consensus about the need for central Government coupled with the need for accountability for its actions. One still has some arguments on the Left and Right politically about, for example, whether to privatise the National Health Service, but neither the Tories nor the Labour Party in the UK have adopted policies of complete privatisation or complete public ownership. There is more agreement between the main political parties than is sometimes apparent. The relatively short-lived domination of the Labour Party by Jeremy Corbyn threatened a much wider programme of public ownership across health and infrastructure activities, but, for the moment at least, this seems to be less prominent. Nevertheless, as just stated, there will obviously be a variation of views on what society needs. Hence, as well as the relevance of Identity, Competitive Environment, Innovation and Collaboration as a framework for Government's own evaluation of its activity, such an analytical structure is also appropriate for those holding Government to account. Even where those wishing to make the Government accountable have quite opposing views on how these concepts might be implemented, identifying differences in them from those held by the Government would be a valuable way of clarifying debates about accountability. Those in power and those wishing to hold them accountable need to undertake a significant amount of analysis to ensure that the accountability process is itself fair from all points of view. This applies even if, in practice, it takes place and evolves on an incremental basis and the focus of attention shifts from time to time reflecting changing needs and events.

All this discussion implies a substantial role for central Government planning, although this does *not* mean that central Government should carry out the implementation of activity. It is argued by Ridley,[233] however,

---

[233] M Ridley, *The evolution of everything*, HarperCollins, 2015, especially chapter 13. His view also chimes well with his recent book on Innovation as discussed above.

that we should beware central planning and that public policies fail from 'planners excessive faith in deliberate design'[234] and he quotes Carswell[235] that the elite gets things wrong 'because they seek to govern by design a world that is best organised spontaneously from below' and that 'they consistently underrate the merits of spontaneous, organic arrangements and fail to recognise that the best plan is often not to have one'. However, such views should be considered very carefully. My argument in this pamphlet is that Government has clear responsibilities in a number of areas discussed above. Both it and its critics need a framework for deciding where competition and collaboration should occur for each of these main responsibilities. The Government should decide how the Ridley/Carswell view should be interpreted. It may decide to leave response to many threats and planning for a wide range of associated issues to other levels of society while retaining strong central direction where needed. There needs to be a conscious and justified decision based on the sort of debate I have proposed. The Government should see that the necessary planning is taking place, even if it does not do it itself.

Recent articles in the press by Lord Sumption and others have warned that actions taken by the current Government[236] to exercise central control over the coronavirus crisis seem to be too authoritarian with too much secrecy about the Government's reasons for actions.[237] Such articles call for a more open debate, especially in Parliament. The proposals being made in this text would agree with Sumption, provided they are subject to the need for haste

---

[234] Many feel that excessive reliance was put upon uncertain science over the coronavirus issue.

[235] D Carswell, *The End of Politics and the Birth of iDemocracy*, Biteback, 2012.

[236] November, 2020.

[237] It is interesting to observe that some journalists have wondered whether the extensive financial support given during the coronavirus crisis will lead to a much more widespread expectation of the Government to provide for needs which might indicate a move towards socialism. (Once things are provided it may be difficult to take them away). This is a separate matter from Government accountability and one does not expect philosophers to support any particular political ideology, but they might consider under what circumstances the population swings from right to left or vice versa.

and secrecy where needed on some issues. Janet Daley[238] has expressed a more severe warning in suggesting that recent Government decision-making might lead to a move away from democracy towards totalitarianism. I suppose they might, but a clear distinction needs to be made between an overall ideology about the degree of democracy allowed or central authority applied and the need to consider the degree of centrality and collaboration needed to deal with each major threat. Some threats, not many one hopes, do need to be dealt with in a centralised way. Some even benefit from a suspension of politics and operation as a coalition across political parties. The degree of collaboration required and between whom needs to be related to the nature of the threat. This is not meant to imply that the Government acted correctly or incorrectly. There are clearly many differing views on this question. My point is that a decision framework is needed for dealing with each area of Government and the major crises that occur in each area. Broad arguments about democracy and totalitarianism do little to resolve such crises. Philosophers were prominent in sorting out what democracy and the general role of Government should be. In my opinion they can promote similar progress by helping decision makers to analyse what subordinate parts of Government should be doing and balancing priorities between them.

The whole discussion in this section of this text has focused on the Central Government's role and its accountability, but the process of governing takes place at many levels in society, including companies, charities and even at family level. Exactly the same needs to consider Identity, Competitive Environment, Empathy, Innovation and Collaboration apply at all these levels. These concepts seem to be the fundamental concepts relating to the operation of any group. In discussing leadership in companies, Ridley[239] says that what really works inside a big firm is division of labour and good management means the coordination of the resultant actions. That is precisely the point. Analysis of each activity is needed to employ the right degree of coordination (and collaboration). The critical word in the quotation from Carswell is 'often'. But then the critical question is when is

---

[238] *Sunday Telegraph*, 1 November 2020.

[239] Ridley, op cit, Chapter 12.

planning acceptable; what does 'often' mean? Often central planning may be detrimental, but on occasion there will be the need for considerable central direction and planning. The obvious examples are in times of war or major pandemics. Even then too much emphasis may be placed on central decision-making and insufficient recognition made of what individual private contributions could be made to resolving the problem if encouraged to exercise their own initiative. Indeed, some have said just this regarding the recent coronavirus crisis. It is, however, inconceivable that the Government should have taken little or no action or planning in such a situation. Even at the level of the private family, some direction and planning for the future is needed together with the appropriate degree of freedom of roles within the family. The key, for *any* form of government must be, to find the right balance between direction, planning and 'letting go'. While at the family level this will be largely intuitive, for large organisations and central Government careful analysis is needed.

9.

Language

I must admit at the outset of this section that I was very aware of my lack of knowledge of the philosophy of language. Kenny addresses this principally in his volumes 2 and 4, introducing the reader to topics such as the types of different words, the use of ostensive observation (pointing to objects) in learning words (Augustine), the failure of ostensiveness to describe all words, the relation between logic and language, the difference between the *reference* and *sense* of words (Frege), syntactic (grammar), semantics (how language relates to reality), pragmatics (the purposes and consequences of language in context), the difference between private and public language (Wittgenstein) and so on. It is clear that there is a massive literature spreading back over centuries on this topic and with which I will never become conversant, let alone understand all its nuances. Nevertheless, I fall back upon the main purpose in constructing these notes which was to clarify what I held in my mind when considering each of the main areas of philosophy addressed by Kenny. What do I, as a layman, consider language to be? And how does that influence the way I look out into the world? So how do I view the topic of language?

My first thought was that language is not a concept that should be considered in isolation. I suppose this places my views closest to the pragmatists listed above. Language exists for a purpose and its main purpose is communication between people through the use of words.[240] Indeed it is the main and most sophisticated method of communicating. It is not, however, the only form of communication. One may think that I mean something like semaphore or Morse code, but these are really the use of alternative symbols to the usual alphabet to form the same words and so they are not really a different form of communication to language. They are

---

[240] Indeed, some communication occurs between people and pet animals where the latter seem to understand a very limited vocabulary of words.

a different form of transmission of the same language. Nevertheless, they are useful in reminding us that there are physical forms of communication other than speech or writing.

Kenny also describes how Augustine outlines the way children use facial expressions and eye and body movement to try to communicate their wishes before they acquire some linguistic ability.[241] The term 'body language' is also well used in modern times. It is clear that facial expression or other bodily movements can be used to support words being used, modify or contradict their meaning or even be used in place of them. It is important to note this when discussing later how language developed.

While the main purpose of language is communication between members of society, it is not the only purpose. My thinking is, in the main, undertaken using a socially constructed English language. I have no intention of communicating a lot of this thinking with others. I am not just referring to theorising in an academic sense, but each of us is embarked on a whole continuing series of thoughts through each day. The more complex and novel the thoughts, the more we use language internally to put them in some sort of order. Even so, we must still take care. We can do thinking without words. Evidence of this is obvious in animals which do not have a verbal language, but they do have brains and, depending on the type of animal, communicate by means of scent, posture, touch, sound and electrical discharges. A pride of lions[242] can organise a hunt without verbal language. They know that they are hungry, spy an antelope and, through training and learning derived from their parents, also without words, *collectively* track it down and make a kill. Dawkins[243] details how many different types of animals and birds communicate and how that is related to survival and is of benefit to both the sender and the recipient. Later in the same book, he also discusses whether animals can lie. This apparently is of critical importance

---

[241] They often demonstrate their feelings through bodily actions, sometimes quite stridently, long after acquiring linguistic skills. This applies to some adults too.

[242] Lions are not alone in having this capability. For example, sea lions have been known to hunt in packs for tuna fish.

[243] R Dawkins, *The Selfish Gene*, op cit, p 63.

to some philosophers in judging whether such communication is really language. In my view the key point is whether human language developed from earlier and more basic forms of communication such as that needed to coordinate hunting. I cannot see how it could have been otherwise.

Recent research suggests that, millions of years before Man developed language, primates, who had no language, could 'connect' non-adjacent sounds (that is preceded words) to gain meaning. Man, presumably, gradually developed a more elaborate set of sounds whose meaning became generally accepted amongst the community in which he was embedded. Spikins[244] also refers to Dunbar[245] who argued that language then developed not just to coordinate and think, but because we need to gossip in order to discuss and evaluate the motivations, trustworthiness and reputation of others and convince others of our goodwill. This required much more subtlety than coordinating signals for hunting in groups. This together with the later development of writing and reading led to our modern human languages.

Prior to Wittgenstein, the notion of private ostensive definition was paramount in the philosophy of language. This meant that one observed something with which one was familiar and named it as a private mental act. Wittgenstein stressed that such a private language is impossible. Such thinking takes place within a society with a language that is already there. It is publicly available. As Kenny says:

> The upshot of Wittgenstein's argument is that there cannot be a language whose words refer to what can *only* be known to the individual speaker of the language. The English word 'pain' is not a word in a private language … it is not by private ostensive definition that 'pain' becomes the name of the sensation; pain-language is grafted onto the pre-linguistic expression of pain when parents teach a baby to replace her initial cries with a conventional, learned expression through language.

Kenny states that it was this demolition of the notion of a private language

---

[244] P Spikins, *How compassion made us human*, op cit, pp 192–3.
[245] R Dunbar, Gossip in evolutionary perspective, *Review of General Psychiatry*, 8 (2) 2004, pp 100–110.

by Wittgenstein that was the most significant event in the philosophy of language in the 20th century. Wittgenstein showed that acquaintance with an object that was referred to in a word or sentence was insufficient to gain an understanding of meaning. That required seeing that word in context within social activities and what he called 'language games'.

While Wittgenstein certainly had very perceptive insights into what language is and how it is *operated*, his analysis does not seem to be adequate in explaining how language *developed*. This must have been as an emergent activity. He does not, as far as I am aware, provide an explanation of the dynamics by which we arrived at our languages of the present day. The vast majority of what we say and write uses established words with a sufficiently common meaning given to them by agreement in society, but language does evolve. How does this happen? New words cannot be constructed by all members of society at the same time. Words also enter usage from other languages. So, at least, there is not one ubiquitous common public, but a series of publics. An entirely new word or word usage can only come into existence if someone, or some small subset of the public, coins that new word or phrase as a *proposed* language act. It then is lost or gradually adopted by the wider society. This has also become evident in the new digital age where a plethora of new terms have come into daily usage, often to refer to quite new objects or phenomena, but surely it also applies to all variations in language. Teenagers are continually inventing new meanings for words if not new words themselves. There must have been someone or a small group that decided that 'cool' would now mean 'that's great!' before it became adopted in wider use. Moreover, even if we acknowledge that our thinking takes place using a publicly accepted language, we cannot be sure that everyone hearing/seeing that language interprets a word in exactly the same way even where the context is specified.

To some extent our private interpretation of the public word is involved in our thinking. All we can ensure is that there is sufficient commonality of understanding for the phrase to make sense for the interaction between the particular speaker/writer and the listener/reader involved. While evidently applicable for most communication, I wonder, therefore, whether Wittgenstein's demolition of the possibility of 'private language', as accepted by Kenny, should not be modified. Such modification should take into account, first, the process by which changes in language occur over time and, second, the variations around the consensus core meaning of a word in interpretations by each individual. There is not a simple private/public language dichotomy with only the public version left standing when the private was demolished. There is scope for *some, probably really quite limited,* private and semi-private (small group) development of language and it is, at least to some extent, the interaction of this private with public language that leads to the evolution of the latter at the margin. To fully understand the use of language, one must recognise that it is dynamic and always changing and expanding even if only at the margin and there must be some specific trigger for that change.

The mention of evolution brings me to Kenny's view on how language first developed. It is clear that language became very important as a device to improve the functioning of social groups and then wider societies – probably beginning about 2 million years ago. But how did this evolve? Some comments have already been made at the beginning of this section of the text, but to relate it to philosophy it now needs to be explored in more depth.

In an earlier section of these notes it was explained how Darwin's Theory of Evolution cannot be used to explain the origin of life and the origin of the universe. Kenny argues that, also, it cannot be used to explain the origin of language. Given the introduction of the notion of evolving language above, it is interesting to address this issue.

Kenny argues[246] that Darwin's idea of natural selection presupposes a genetically derived physical feature of some individuals which gives them an advantage. While there is no problem in identifying some individuals as having, say, longer legs, Kenny says that there is a problem with the idea that a single language user occurred by genetic variation. It is difficult to conceive, continues Kenny, of how anyone could be described as a language user before there was a community of language users.[247] This is clearly correct, but he

---

[246] pp 302–4, Volume 4, op cit.

[247] Kenny reaffirmed his view on this within the debate involving him, Richard Dawkins and Rowan Williams (then Archbishop of Canterbury) at the Sheldonian, Oxford, 23 February

also says that human language is a rule-governed, communal activity, totally different from the signalling systems to be found in non-humans. He even carries his argument further by adding that language cannot be the result of trial and error learning because such learning presupposes stable goals and there is no goal in acquiring a language because one needs a language to express that wish.

First, there *is* a clear objective in acquiring a language – it is communication.[248] A babe is aware that it wants to communicate, but, at that stage of its life, it does *not* have language and uses body motion and eye movement to try to convey its wishes as Augustine observed centuries ago. There **is** trial and error involved in this process of communication, but this is not yet in language. The baby learns that certain sounds will gain parental attention and the provision of comfort and/or food. The baby does not need language to know that it is hungry and that, if it does not communicate this, it will not survive. In a Wittgenstein sense, it just acts. The child first attempts certain sounds and bodily movements and soon sees what sounds and body language the parent understands and to which it reacts. He/she later acquires language in the same way by perceiving the 'public language' already used by adults and copying them in order to achieve its goal of better communication.

Moreover, I do wonder whether human language is so different from signalling systems in non-humans. I would rather see human languages at the more sophisticated end of a continuum of signalling systems used by all organisms that possess life. Primitive life has primitive signalling. Chimpanzees will have better signalling than other animal groups. Some animals will have totally different signalling systems; perhaps based just on actions and sounds which humans cannot replicate. By studying non-human 'discourse' through signalling, I am sure that rules or at least standard practices could equally be observed. Otherwise the communication would not work. There has to be some recognisable form. The fact that human

---

2012. Incidentally, I had completed the first draft of these notes prior to becoming aware of this debate and watching a video of it. I then added this footnote as a postscript. The debate did not seem to provide anything which gave me cause to revise anything I have written in these notes.

[248] How can the attempt to learn a foreign language not be in pursuit of an objective?

languages are built on rules that are much more detailed and sophisticated, with complex grammar, than non-human signalling systems does not make them the only possessors of rules. Hence, language is not *fundamentally* different in basic concept from signalling systems throughout the animal kingdom. I am sure biologists could substantiate this.

Now, while there is a variety of signalling systems across the animal kingdom, how did those dependent on sound arise? It must have been through genetic variation over millions of years. It must be the physical variation in the brain/voice box combination that leads to differing animal capabilities to develop sound signalling in different forms. At some very distant point in the past, therefore, the human genus divided off by genetic variation from its common ancestry with chimpanzees. This gave humans the ability to develop communication in the form that chimpanzees do not have. From then on, humans strove to improve communication from using simple bodily signalling and grunts to the point where more elaborate sounds became the dominant method.

Subsequently, human societies developed rules to standardise sounds, standardise the meaning of those sounds and, eventually, develop rules of grammar to facilitate to recognise the difference between actions (verbs), objects (nouns), descriptors (adjectives), certainty (assertions) and possibility (if statements) to enable more sophisticated spoken and written interactions. Of course this was a social development activity. From probably about 6,000 years ago, human forms of spoken communication then spread into the written forms of language where even more extensive rules were developed, initially it is believed, to keep records of events and later as a means of communicating over distances where both sides of the communication need not be present and even later into a means of setting thoughts down (such as in these notes) for any other interested party to read. This process of writing language is still continuing and developing in the digital age.

This long-run development of human signalling systems probably began to accelerate in earnest about 2 million years ago as wider social groups formed and human brain size increased.[249] All of this was encouraged by the

---

[249] See Section 3 of these notes.

need for collaboration in order to survive in a competitive world as discussed in previous sections. There was an interplay between the development of society, language and brain size. As stated earlier, I do not think that the rapid growth of brain size between 7 and 2 million years ago has been adequately explained to date, but the fact that it occurred does facilitate an explanation of the development of societies and their languages.

Kenny is obviously right in stating that an individual could not have evolved genetically as a fully-fledged language user before society had developed that language, but this is just a truism. It does not probe how the social activity of using language itself evolved gradually from more basic forms of communication and the way it evolved *was* enabled by genetic legacies in the human brain and voice box. Some humans, did make use of their better human brain power and vocal powers given by them by genetic variation to develop improvement in communication and, eventually, language.

At the embryonic stage in the development of speech there simply was not an established public language in which to undertake this initial thinking. Communication, initially, must have involved as body signalling systems. Agreed public speech must have started with ideas initiated in the private, or in the very small group, domain with testing and then consensus amongst small social groups which led gradually to the establishment of an accepted public language. Each successive generation of humans with common genetic features used the form of public language developed before them, but then developed public languages further. At each subsequent stage the language developer would have undertaken his/her thinking in the language that existed at that time in the locality within which he/she was located and then extended that public, but local, language by an interaction between private and public language. Each addition to language must have occurred in the private, or very local, domain because at that time it was not publicly available. Over time ever wider social groups needed communication in a form which combined the local languages. This process is continuing today, as evidenced by the very rapid spread of usage of English throughout the world. From the initial genetic variation which provided a capability for developing human language through to the present day, each stage in that development process provided an advantage of some sort or another for the society employing the language. At times this may have provided a better basis for organising activities and surviving[250] and much later this also provided the basis for improved cultural interaction and some forms of aesthetics. But it seems that there must have usually been an evolutionary advantage for the development.

As Kenny says, Wittgenstein achieved a major step forward in emphasising that language is publicly available to us, rather than privately generated, and also that the vast majority of private thinking must take place in a 'public language' given to us in our own context. He was right. I would just modify the statements *at the margin* to argue for a supporting role of 'private language' in the *evolution* of language and also stress that all human thinking is not totally dependent on our existing language – though most of it is. But I also think that Kenny does not sufficiently consider language as one branch, albeit a very sophisticated one, of communication systems and, particularly, as a dynamic phenomenon developing over millions of years. He does not recognise, at least explicitly in his cited volumes, that it must have been human genetic variation that subsequently *enabled* improved communication through the form of language. Obviously, genetic variation could not have suddenly provided Man with language, but it enabled societies possessing that variation to develop its 'public language'.

The Value of Language Beyond Communication

The argument above focused mainly on the use of language for communication with some occasional reference to it being the foundation of most human thinking. This latter aspect of the use of language also needs deeper consideration. Clearly, when we think, we automatically think of words associated with the actions, objects or arguments. If I look at the table at which I am typing, I think of the pens, diary, spectacles and a telephone resting on the table. Words, are therefore, a way of simplifying and summarising what I see. I do not say there is a lot of folded paper, pinned

---

[250] This may have applied centuries ago. The thought of secret codes employed in wartime and still in use today come to mind.

together and marked out with dates and covered in a hard cardboard cover which is itself covered in soft leather-like material. I see a diary. Through repetitive use they enter our long-term memories and serve as a shorthand for the much more extended descriptions that otherwise would be needed. What applies to objects, also seems to apply for words about actions. Words, therefore, enable us to think and act more efficiently. They influence the thinking process.

The use of human language enables us to argue verbally in spoken or written form. In the process of argument there is an interplay between humans where thoughts of one are presented to the other. This quite often leads to a modification of thoughts of one or both parties. This is so, even if I am sitting alone trying to think through an issue or writing this text. I am writing an argument with 'an assumed other' who will be evaluating my thoughts. I may even decide on contemplation that 'this assumed other (s)' may have much better arguments than mine that I refrain from making them public. The use of words and language interacts with the Mind, not just by modifying neural networks to record shorthand symbols as indicated above, they actually affect thought processes themselves. They also enable the development of thought. Usually, when writing, I have some initial idea of what I want to write, but it is only through setting thoughts in words that I get further ideas. The very process of writing suggests further thoughts.[251] The process of reading provides a more obvious example of how language and words affect our thinking. Language and words act as, in what Clark[252] calls, 'language as scaffolding'. He addresses this issue technically in a lot more depth than I do here.

> The linguistic scaffoldings that surround us and that we ourselves create, are both cognition enhancing in their own right and help to provide the tools we use to discover and build the myriad other props and scaffoldings whose cumulative effect is to press minds like ours from the biological flux.

---

[251] There may be more scope for this in social sciences rather than in the physical sciences, but I am not sure.

[252] A Clark, *Supersizing the Mind*, op cit, Chapter 3.

The Use of Language to Influence the Thought of Others

Before leaving the topic of language, it is important, given the space devoted above to developments in political philosophy and Government actions, to consider how language may be used, not just as a general communication device, but as a means of exercising control and influencing behaviour. The exact way in which thoughts and instructions are expressed and the selection of words made rather than just the provision of information, does influence behaviour. A trivial example is the phenomenon of telling lies. This may be, say, by small children or adults in trying to escape responsibility and perhaps punishment for some act. It is, however, of much more significance where those in authority wish to get support for and justify a particular type of behaviour.

A very good example recently is the Government's repetitive use daily of the slogan: *Stay Home; Support the NHS; Save Lives.* In attempting to stop the spread of coronavirus, it was decided that members of society had to isolate themselves at home. It was also obviously thought that many would not observe a bland message saying that this is what is needed. Indeed, such isolation was very distressing for some. The Government clearly felt that the message had to be drummed in on television every day with a very clear and simple slogan to try to ensure widespread adoption. Language therefore, involves not just choice of phrasing and words, but also the emphasis put upon words and the way they are used – in this case repetitively.[253] This is just one example of many political or Governmental statements that could be quoted.

While in previous Sections of this text, it has been demonstrated how identity, competition, collaboration, ethics and political action are all closely interrelated as a part of the total social system, it must be recognised that language is an important part of this system. Political control may, to some extent, be achieved by force, penalties and rewards, but, primarily it is

---

[253] And many now argue that this was overdone so much that it has installed fear to deviate from this action into many people at a time when the Government is now urging a return, at least partially, to an active life outside of the home.

through the use of language and persuasion. In due course Governments in Western democracies have to account to the electorate and then language is the vehicle for persuasion.

Recently Fraser Nelson[254] drew attention to Boris Johnson's attributes that admirably captures how language can be used to exercise control. Nelson argues for Johnson to change his emphasis on language from the *Stay Home and Save the NHS* warning to be more proactive in encouraging people to promote economic recovery. To quote:

> It's not unkind to say that Boris Johnson stands for boosterism: a belief that you can talk things into being, that words can shape events. His recent biography of Winston Churchill was obsessed with this

Nelson continues that Johnson[255] wrote that Churchill:

> ... had the gift of language to put heart into people ... to mobilise the English Language and give courage to others

The controlling use of language may, in contrast, be misused. Having just read Klemperer's three volumes[256] of diary covering the mid-30s to mid-50s, he shows how the Nazi regime used language to keep the German people ignorant of the state of the war. He also emphasises how Nazi language was developed to encourage many Aryan Germans to despise and mistreat Jews and, indeed, justify Hitler and his aides murdering thousands of them. It is one thing to be interested in the way language developed. It is also very important to realise how language can be used to change peoples' perception of reality.

Klemperer also describes how he thought much of the Stalinist language and propaganda after the end of the Second World War was of a similar

---

[254] *Daily Telegraph*, 28 August 2020.

[255] Perhaps Johnson's view is derived from his classical education and awareness that rhetoric was recognised a key personal skill in Rome.

[256] V Klemperer, Volume 1, *I shall bear witness*, 1933–41, Volume 2, *To the Bitter End*, 1942–45 and Volume 3, *The Lesser Evil*, 1945–59. Klemperer was widely acclaimed for his *Lingua Terti Imperii* (Language of the Third Reich) – a study of Nazi language – and followed this up with *Lingua Quarti Imperii*, drawing out similarities.

dictatorial type. Despite joining the Communist Party in East Germany after the war, Klemperer says a large picture of Stalin reminded him of Hermann Göring. Of course, this may now be considered an extreme use of language to exercise control. But all Governments, and probably most large companies too, employ corporate language to embed their views on the way their citizens and employees should act. They use language to try to establish a clear unchallengeable identity. Also, at the level of the individual, it is not unknown for parents to use language as a means of control!

Finally, it is important to recognise the part played by public information in the critical review of Government decisions. It is of note how, in this process, the expression of language and perceptions of reality is still evolving. It has always been possible for lies to be told and different words and emphasis used to express ideas and gain power or political advantage, but the advent of social media has added a considerable dimension to this practice. Recent years have seen a massive expansion of available information through the widespread distribution and use of computing and emergence of social media like Twitter and Facebook. In order to obtain well-informed debate and review of Government policy and decisions it is imperative that these forms of information are effectively operated and monitored and yet there are reasons why we should often view such information sceptically. One can put data on the internet so easily now and circulate it almost immediately worldwide that it is impossible to check the validity of all that is on the web. Currently, the vast majority of this information is probably correct and useful and leading to rapid advances in knowledge for many of us, but falsehoods also can easily be circulated to influence those who too readily believe what they read. While there has always been the possibility of issuing 'fake news',[257] before the very widespread development of social media via the internet, there was a limit to which indoctrination could occur through giving deliberately misleading information. Now anyone can publish almost whatever they like with the knowledge that they will not be accountable for their statements.

---

[257] Hitler was pretty good at it, but it was not confined to him as the Allies tried to mislead the enemy as to military strategy and such practices have taken place for many years and not just for military reasons.

This raises a very important question for democracies. Accountability has been shown historically to be fundamental to such a political system. Yet, if modern developments mean that language and information offered to render accountability is misleading, no one is properly accountable and the system threatens to break down. Also those offering misleading information are not sufficiently accountable. Considerable attention needs to be paid to this situation. It is a new and modern problem that is not a straightforward to solve. The very existence of social media outlets depends upon allowing their users to be as free as possible to express what they like and circulate it widely. At the same time those media outlets want to avoid issuing false information. The importance of this was emphasised when, in 2017, both Facebook and Twitter claimed that thousands of Americans had been exposed to thousands of pieces of Russian-backed political information posted by Russia. There was also the suspicion that Russia had tried to influence the outcome of the Presidential election in 2016. Both of these social media outlets have also had reason to question whether they should allow some posts by the US President himself. Twitter, Facebook and other media firms too are addressing this issue. They have said that they have recently taken action to prevent 'fake news' being posted on the coronavirus, but there is still public criticism that Facebook, for example, is still complacent in the spread of misinformation. So should the private sector media firms be left to police themselves or should there be tougher laws? This is not a completely new issue. It has always existed for newspapers, but the difference now is that anyone now can publish virtually what he or she likes. In fact, the issue goes far beyond just 'fake news'. Hateful propaganda can scare or incite people to act inappropriately. This danger is also likely to become greater unless real care is taken to control developments.

The control of language may become even more problematic. Recent advances in Artificial Intelligence (AI), such as the emergence of the GPT-3 human language generator, suggest that much of what we read may become generated by computer algorithms rather than by humans. 'Fake news' is a problem now, but it will become a massive problem if computer-generated text, looking like a very realistic version of human language, produces immense quantities of false information distorting our knowledge and attempting to persuade us to act in a given way. The question of freedom of expression versus control over citizens and public order will have an entirely new dimension with the arrival of advance AI using social media. Where will accountability lie for untrue statements that are produced by AI and circulated widely? Will such computer-generated false information only be detectable and controllable by yet other computer algorithms? How will humans be able to know whether this control is effective? Will we be able ever to know what is true? Can we rely on computers to control computers? If this occurs, as well as providing a vehicle for widespread manipulation of action, it will concern the democratic basis, and even the viability, of our political system. Political philosophers have some tortuous issues to address in terms of the developing use of language in this area.

10.

Conclusions

My initial motivation for attempting this exercise, was to probe my own tacitly held 'philosophies' using Kenny's four volumes as a guide to the philosophical themes to be covered and to consider to what extent it explained my own behaviour.[258] As I undertook the exercise, I realised that my 'philosophies' were developing and deepening as I read both Kenny and some subsequent literature in both philosophy and science. As emphasised in the last Section, the actual process of using language and words influence our neural systems and thoughts, creating a continually revised perception of our world. In a strict sense, therefore, it is impossible to specify our tacit assumptions completely because, in attempting to do so, they will inevitably be modified to some degree. Nevertheless, to attempt to set out the tacit assumptions that I literally held at the outset of this exercise, I should, perhaps, have first tried, without too much new reasoning or attention to additional literature, to write my tacit assumptions down simply using only Kenny's chapter headings as guides to philosophical areas to be covered.[259] Then, afterwards, use Kenny[260] and other literature to see whether I should revise my assumptions. However, for better or worse, that is not what I did. Even so, I believe that I can, in these conclusions, summarise my current views on the areas of philosophy addressed in this text and give a general indication where my understanding has been developed. I do not do this because I think my views are very important. I do it because it shows, as I intended initially, to state what one layman thinks as he tries to make sense

---

[258] One of Kenny's declared objectives in writing his books was to stimulate interest in non-philosophers. He certainly achieved that goal as far as I am concerned.

[259] Of course, writing down dispositions means that literally they are no longer tacit. Also to write implies some thinking and choice of words which itself can lead to development of disposition beyond the initial tacit assumption. So expressing tacit assumptions is problematic. Perhaps, strictly, they can only be deduced from behaviour.

[260] And I had already read Kenny's four volumes when I decided to embark on this exercise.

of philosophy. I state now, however, that I do not think the development in my views will lead to much significant change in everyday behaviour on my part.

Brief Summary on Different Areas of Philosophy

Regarding Section 2 of this text, I felt that Kenny made a major omission of his review of modern philosophy (Volume 4) when he excluded developments in science, particularly relating to our growing knowledge of the universe and space-time and also to the evolution of the species. Surely, our sense of identity must be affected by our understanding of the universe in which we are located. Developments in *physical and biological science* must have a major impact upon our understanding of Epistemology, Metaphysics, Philosophy of the Mind, and the possible nature and existence of God or intelligent controller of the universe.

Kenny[261] says that Wittgenstein was correct in seeing the task of philosophy as completely different from that of empirical science. This would seem to be so, insofar as Metaphysics is *defined* as providing an understanding of matters which are inaccessible to physical science. Physical science is, however, rapidly advancing both the depth and range of knowledge of our universe and our part in it, such that it is reducing some of the scope of interpretation left to Metaphysics. Alternatively, in contrast to Kenny and Wittgenstein, one may say that Metaphysics and physical science do have the same goal, namely that of understanding our universe and our part in it. Kenny's and Wittgenstein's argument, though, takes primacy when considering topics in the latter half of this text: some, but not all, aspects of Mind, ethics, aesthetics, political philosophy and language. It is likely that these subjects will never be completely reducible to empirical algorithms devoid of human choice and taste. But, even here care should be taken. As stated earlier, it may be possible, *eventually*, to use physical science to explain how the human brain generates intentions and makes choices and, together with this, more reliable scientific approaches may also be developed

---

[261] Kenny, op cit, Volume 4, p 143.

to analyse how different ethical or political behaviours have an impact or even how different aesthetic joys are created within humans. If progress is achieved in these areas, the scope and need for a non-scientific dimension of Metaphysics would be reduced.

A deeper consideration of scientific thought on how evolution occurred would help to satisfy philosophers, like Nagel and Midgley, who criticise the Selfish Gene Theory and argue that there must have been a role for teleological laws in explaining evolution. As regards my own learning, prior to this study, I held the view that the Selfish Gene was the explanation of evolution. I now believe that it should be possible to unify scientific thought on evolution based on Darwinian Theory, the Selfish Gene, Genetic Drift and Recombination with philosophical thought on human and other intentions in order to gain a better understanding of evolution. I do not see, however, what grounds there are for introducing teleological laws of the universe. Also, we may be at the stage of evolution where human choice becomes far more significant in the future evolution of our own and other species. In fact, the model of the evolution of life is very similar to a model of social evolution as discussed later in this Section.

In terms of detailed conclusions arrived at in Section 2, the review of our biological evolution served to emphasise the centrality of competition to all of our behaviour. Then the review of the nature of the universe suggested that all matter, including ourselves, is an excitation of energy within one or a number of force fields. And that this must have relevance for considering what God could be in Section 3. However, while this Section explains what, at the most fundamental level, we are comprised of, that is not the perception we have of ourselves and for very practical reasons we can leave this aside and get on with our lives. It was also interesting that *some* feel that QFT means that there is, in reality, no arc-shaped universe of four dimensions and that we can treat, at least for practical purposes, matter as having the traditional three dimensions and that the concept of time can be used just as a measure of change.

Moving on to the consideration of *God and Religion* in Section 3, I had not considered before how separate the concept of God is from the concept of Religion. Previously, I was quite aware that I was an agnostic regarding the existence of God. As argued earlier in the text, however, I feel that those who declare themselves to be agnostics (probably a large proportion of the population) should attempt to consider what possible form God could take given emerging scientific knowledge of our universe. I concluded that it could only be as a type of force field (spirit if you like) or some form of physical existence beyond our universe or set of universes. I consider both of these possibilities to be most unlikely, but I do not know. It is in that way that I am an agnostic. In fact, I am now almost ready to declare that I am an atheist. I say 'almost' because I am just hedging my bets in case these most unlikely conditions for the existence of God do exist.

Clearly very many people, including scientists, claim a belief in God so that should not be dismissed too lightly. I personally doubt the existence of a supreme intelligence or God. I find that those who simply say that God exists because they *feel* that he[262] does are simply failing to address the issue adequately. I cannot see how faith can depend upon such a fragile basis. At the very least, however, the advance of science over the last century must lead us to ask what form, if a supreme intelligence does exist, a God could *possibly* take. If God does exist, he cannot possibly be in the form as conceived in the Bible and elsewhere over centuries. Of course, believers may say that the concept of God is so mysterious that they cannot be expected to guess even what form he might take, but they just believe in a supreme being and some sense of goodness in the universe. In most areas of debate such an attitude would be to admit defeat. Leaders of religion should address this issue more openly and rigorously. One should also be aware, however, that ideas such as General Relativity Theory, quantum physics and even the 'Big Bang' have not yet been established beyond all doubt, nor are they completely consistent with each other. One could, therefore, argue that when we have a certain view of what our universe is, we may have different way of perceiving how God might exist. That seems very unlikely, but it cannot be dismissed logically. Irrespective of all this, however, the existence

---

[262] For convenience I use 'He' to refer to God, although 'She' should not be excluded, or even 'It'. If God takes a completely different form there is no reason why it should be either male or female as we conceive it or completely devoid of sexual orientation.

or otherwise of God does *not*, in my view, have a strong bearing on the value of Religion.

Previously, I failed to understand how leaders of religion could spend so long in church and other religious gatherings going through extensive ritual and, effectively, acting with subservience to an unknowable entity like God. Is there a need for such possible fiction to justify the ethical and other advice gained from religious teachers? Do they really need this fictional authority as God's representatives to persuade their flock to act in a better way? As a consequence of separating out God from Religion, I now recognise more clearly the value and purpose of religion in society, especially if it can be shorn of much of its parading, processing and public prayer, which seems meaningless, and claiming direction from a unique God (separate for each religion!).

Intelligent religious leaders, and indeed some political leaders, may declare a faith in their God, but I wonder how often they are prepared, in private, to question the validity of their faith. Do they simply adopt a public declaration of faith in God because they feel it is necessary to do so to justify the wider good of Religion? Religious leaders would have a more valuable role in society if they focused their activity more on helping to ensure that *all* sides of ethical arguments were fully taken into account in both personal and political issues. They could be established as the one, dominant authority, independent of political parties or the media, that could operate at a broader level than the law courts. Religion *is a social activity* created by Man, not by God. It will continue to evolve, with or without Him, as society and knowledge develops. It would be interesting to see what it has become in 200 years hence.

As far as my own behaviour is concerned, I see no need for change in my non-observance of formal religious practices. I would now urge religious leaders to play more of a leading role as the nation's independent conscience free of historical dogma, provided they can train themselves adequately for the task of making unbiased evaluations.

My thinking about topics in Section 4 were advanced considerably in this exercise. I had not previously spent much effort thinking about the *Mind, Consciousness and Identity*. My tacit assumption was that my Mind was a separate internal entity governing my thinking, actions and reactions to physical stimuli. I was aware of Descartes' views, but never believed that the Mind existed beyond the body. It was therefore very interesting to come upon Clark's book[263] arguing for the Mind to be extended to incorporate all sorts of external influences. I can totally accept his view that the Mind, both neurologically and biologically, is operating within and being influenced by its environment, but I think that it is just a matter of definition whether one considers the Mind to be just the internal bodily function or the complete interacting network.

I did come to realise in more depth what I think consciousness is. I probably thought beforehand that it was just awareness. I had also a vague idea that scientists had identified differing roles for various parts of the brain. Before this exercise, I definitely leaned towards a reductionist view of the world with its explanation of the brain through physics. The considerable space devoted earlier to this topic indicates that I had (and still have) much to learn from both science and philosophy on this topic. I was surprised, however, that Kenny's template of Modern Philosophy did not pay more attention to current knowledge of the role of parts of the brain in addressing this issue. It is also clear that both scientists and philosophers are currently trying to establish what consciousness is. People like Crick and Penrose, from quite different perspectives, adopt approaches based on physical science and, apparently, many philosophers are also committed to reductionist theory where they think that a more thorough use of it will yield solutions to the problems of Mind and consciousness.[264] I discovered that other philosophers such as Nagel, Searle and Midgley do not reject reductionist approaches, but say they are not enough; they cannot explain everything.

Nagel et al. do stress, however, that they would like to seek a unified view of these topics involving both reductionist physics and a deeper understanding of the nature of our biological evolution than just given by Darwinism. Science and mental concepts are parts of the same world and

---

[263] A Clark, *Supersizing the Mind*, op cit.

[264] See Nagel, *Mind and Cosmos*, op cit, p 43.

we need a better development of both with scientists developing a further understanding of how the brain works while recognising that such knowledge will not explain what it is like to actually be any given different individual with different experiences. Writing this text has certainly extended my own view on these topics. I am not sure that it will affect how I behave except that it has stimulated me to try to think a lot more about these problems.

Leading on from the concept of consciousness, Section 4 also incorporated a brief consideration of free will and then Identity. On Identity, I conclude that it is ever changing to some extent throughout life, but it is important to understand it for reasons given later in the text.

In Section 5 I was encouraged to think more deeply about *ethics* than I had done previously. As regards ethics, to relate what is perhaps a hackneyed phrase, I have always had a strong instinct to treat others as one would like to be treated oneself.[265] However, my efforts in this Section led me beyond simple interpretation to see the origin of ethics stemming from the need of humans to evolve an organised society and also to see how competitive struggle was related to the development of democracy. The latter aspect could equally have been included in the later Section on political philosophy. It seemed, however, a natural extension of thinking about fairness and, to a large degree, reference here is to historical context here that pre-dates that in the later Section on political philosophy.

Clear distinctions were also made between fairness and compassion, the former being the product of quite rational thought about what is needed for a balanced and organised society, whereas compassion may well have been hard-wired into our brains from a much earlier stage of evolution. Although, if so, I still find it difficult to see how charity towards old folk, however commendable, would assist in survival of the gene. Perhaps compassion is something hard-wired into our DNAs that is a surplus requirement from the perspective of the survival of the genes, but, nevertheless, still operational. Compassion seems also to be closely related to aspects of consciousness and empathy, but I have not been able to explore that.

The material in Section 5 did lead me to recognise the way ethical

---

[265] I am not claiming that I have always managed to observe it.

practice evolved and is multilayered and exists within a structured form that society has for dealing with it. None of this needs to be based upon religion, although religion has played a major part in the evolution of ethical practice. Despite this, I argue that modification of how religions operated could lead to them playing a more proactive and effective role as society's conscience by keeping the ethical structure we have under review.

On reviewing the philosophy on *aesthetics*, in Section 6, I found nothing significantly different from my own philosophy. I always thought that beauty really is in the eye of the beholder, but the eye can be trained. Although many beholders may agree on what constitutes something aesthetically beautiful, one must always allow that other individuals may see things differently and there is no real point in making an issue of it where that occurs. Contemplating the margin between aesthetics and other pleasurable activities did, however, make me realise how important such other pleasures are. In assessing whether one has a worthwhile life this is probably rather more important to most people than intricate arguments about aesthetics. I concluded that aesthetics was just at one end of a continuum ranging from aesthetics to more general recreation and that the level of delight or satisfaction cannot be easily related to a quantitative measure by current scientific practice. Even so, there is scope for much further philosophical and scientific enquiry into how the Mind operates to generate surges of delight or other feelings in response to artistic and recreational stimuli.

While my initial intention was just to identify what I thought about these areas of philosophy, two dominant conclusions became obvious to me that led to a change in emphasis in the second half of the text although still, I think, very relevant to philosophy. The first emerged from considering *together* all the different philosophical fields that I had examined. This led me to propose, in Section 7, an approach to updating the notion of *a worthwhile existence*.

It seemed to me that there was no appropriate universal definition of a worthwhile existence. We, each of us as individuals, have our own notion of what it is. Moreover, this also applies to organisations, Governments, etc. In addition, when considering the areas of science and philosophy addressed in Sections 2 to 6, I realised that this provided me with the framework that we all must use, varying degrees, as basis for all major decision-making (at individual, corporate or state level) in order to achieve a worthwhile existence. I suggest that a framework that requires decision-makers to consider of Identity, Competition, Ethics, Recreation, Empathy, Collaboration, Innovation, as they relate to each major decision situation. At the level of the individual what sort of life does he want (what is his identity), can he be competitive enough to achieve it, will he need to adopt different actions and be innovative to achieve it, what collaboration will be need to do so, can he compete in a fair manner and exercise compassion where needed, can he do all this ensuring he has adequate recreation to satisfy his chosen identity? The extent to which he achieves this will indicate whether he himself thinks he has achieved a worthwhile life. The same could be said for a company or a society as a whole represented by its Government. It seems clear to me that while this framework is offered as a basis for taking key decisions, it is hardly novel. It is actually how decisions are made, underpinned by a combination of concepts from different areas of philosophy. There is, however, no reason why any single entity's decision-making cannot be improved and the five factor framework might be used more explicitly to achieve this.

My initial intention regarding *political philosophy* was to outline development to date and then consider whether my own 'philosophy' had kept pace with such development. However, having written Section 6 dealing with a decision model for a worthwhile existence, it seems a natural progression to see how to apply this to Government activities. As outlined in Section 7, political philosophers were instrumental in showing how the interests of elites needed balancing with those of the not so elite and how central accountability needed to be part of this process. It is obvious that extensive systems of accountability now exist. In holding the Government to account Parliament, Opposition political parties, the Press and Media, the Legal Process all currently play their part. This now seems to be a generally accepted matter in Western democracies and I have no wish to differ from it. The question that remains is how processes of decision-making and accountability might be improved. The review of philosophy on a wider basis beyond political philosophy suggested that political philosophers could help to refine this process by ensuring that all of the five listed judgement criteria: Identity (including ethical disposition and recreational needs), Competition, Innovation, Collaboration, Compassion are all considered fully in resolving issues in each major area of Government activity. This is related to, but separate from, finding the actual solutions to specific political and economic problems. Moreover, I do not wish to suggest that political philosophy is reduced to just a form of corporate decision-making. That would be absurd: there will always be opposing views on goals and how to achieve them and power struggles to gain ascendancy. This would be reflected by deliberating on the identity of those considering Government policy (both for and against) and Governments themselves will always consist of differentiating groups. I merely suggest that, in the way philosophers historically reasoned towards solutions of broader issues, they might also play a more significant part in helping each of the various parties involved to address more specific problems. This is a natural extension of their arguments leading to the establishment of democracy and Government accountability in most countries. They successfully argued how democracy should work. They could now be just as practical in debating just how the main Government services should operate – not at the detailed solution level, but in terms of debates to be raised and considered.

Finally, I came to Section 9 on *Language*. I had not thought much about language before other than it was obviously a means of both spoken and written communication. My review in this text made me aware of Wittgenstein's convincing argument of language as 'public language'. I wonder, however, whether this currently dominant view gives adequate consideration to how language has evolved and continues to evolve from the 'private' to 'public', even if only at the margin.[266] There must be some initial 'private language' input into the development of new words and uses of them, even if most of them are modifications of existing ones. Nevertheless, after any initial adoption of terminology, our language in use becomes clearly 'public language'.

Moving beyond the meaning of words, I am now more aware of how the structure of language influences thought and behaviour, although I am sure that my understanding of this is still at a relatively naive level. I

---

[266] Once again, I need to add a caveat. This may have been addressed in philosophical literature to which I have not been exposed.

also found it interesting to appreciate how our use of language affects our neurological processes. There is, hence, an interplay between language and our consciousness and identity.[267] Finally, I think that a complete insight into the evolution of our language needs to incorporate how it has evolved to become the sophisticated extreme of a continuum stretching from animal communication methods to human use of language. This Section of the text concludes with the use of language to do more than just communicate or facilitate thought and operate as a tool of political and social control even to the extent of 'fake news'.

A Simple Model of Social Evolution

If individuals, organisations and governments make decisions in the way outlined in Section 7, this must be the foundation of how society changes over time. This is not evolution in just the physical Darwinian sense, but evolution of knowledge and understanding of our human condition is taking place all the time with developments in some fields affecting others. One can see quite clearly how thought, acceptable perspectives and practices have developed through time in religion, politics, ethics, language and aesthetics. There is no reason to suppose that this will change. Evolution and change in both physical and social senses is the central philosophy of life. Moreover, I think there is a fairly general model of social evolution that can be built upon the decision structure just stated, but first, it is interesting to consider another view on social evolution:

> There are two ways to tell the story of the twentieth century. You can describe a series of wars, revolutions, crises, epidemics, financial calamities. Or you can point to the gentle but inexorable rise in the quality of life of almost everybody on the planet: swelling income, conquest of disease, the disappearance of parasites, the retreat of want, the increasing persistence of peace, the lengthening of life, the advances in technology. I wrote the whole book about the latter story. *M Ridley*[268]

---

[267] My caveat here is the same as for footnote 214.

[268] M Ridley, *The Evolution of Everything*, op cit.

I think many across the world would argue that they have not had swelling incomes or a peaceful existence, but one can accept that this view applies to most of the civilised world, although there are definitely still pockets of populations that have not fared as well as suggested. However, even granting this, I feel that Ridley (and Wagner) under-emphasise the importance of crises in shaping the path of social or cultural evolution. It is beyond question that major wars, pandemics and revolutions have instigated major changes in society. The Russian and French Revolutions are prime examples, as was the American War of Independence. The two World Wars led to significant change in weaponry, society and politics. The recent coronavirus crisis is bringing about new ways of operating some businesses as well as individual behaviour. Ridley is right to say that new developments which are introduced in these crisis situations are nearly all rooted in innovation that was started some time before, but, in my view, a more complete model of social evolution must incorporate specific reference to crises. Understanding evolution is not just seeing what forces drive development over the long run, but also some recognition of timing and why things occur when they do.

When a crisis occurs, something has to be done and quickly. In the coronavirus crisis, organised nationally supported teams studying vaccines may have been best placed to develop vaccines, but much other innovation is taking place in medicine, lockdown, working from home, restaurants delivery services and so on. They did not come through serendipity or long running thought about a problem. They came from competitive pressure to survive in the new environment. If you run a cafe and then find you have no income there is a pretty strong extrinsic motivation to do something to earn some money. The majority of major scientific and technological breakthroughs have come from intrinsic motivation as Ridley demonstrates repeatedly with his examples. His is a most valuable contribution to our thinking about innovation. Nevertheless, that is not the totality of explaining how evolution works. When a crisis occurs, whether it is at national, company or individual level, action needs to be taken. This suggests quite a simple structure of the process of social evolution.

First, all social entities[269] operate within a COMPETITIVE ENVIRONMENT which is changed by CRISES which in social evolution are like mutations of the genes in physical evolution. Crises occur through NATURAL CAUSES like pandemics, earthquakes or climate change. They also occur through changes in IDENTITIES[270] of those operating in the environment and what they are seeking from it, especially new competitors with new desires. They also occur through new INVENTIONS. New inventions can cause crises for competitors that do not have them and have which become available in the inexorable march forward in innovation that Ridley describes.

In order to survive in this changing environment, entities employ EMPATHY to assess how rivals and all parties affected by the crisis will act. They then must consider their own identity and whether it should be altered. In the case of a company, for example, does it wish to stay in the same markets or move to other ones? Does it want to be seen as operating in one particular manner or to revise its image? Once a company has clarified what Identity it wishes to adopt it must consider what its needs are to remain in effective competition. This may necessitate INNOVATION in products, markets, customers, processes, production inputs, selling strategies or sources of supply. It will then be necessary to consider whether it can go it alone or COLLABORATE with other parties with whom it may already be in collaboration over supply chains, production, marketing or delivery systems, but for a major crisis it will need to review whether changes to this collaborative structure are required. This can be shown diagrammatically as Figure 1 which exhibits a never-ending cycle of evolution.

While competition is stated here in terms of a company competing for a market, the same logic applies to individuals or Governments trying to survive in their environments. Also trying to survive in the face of crises

---

[269] The word 'entities' refers here to all sizes and types of social groupings: Governments, companies, organisations, clubs, charities, group of individuals, individuals, etc. All have a need for survival, perhaps in changed form, and all encounter crises from time to time.

[270] Incorporating both ethical disposition and recreational needs among other goals, strengths and weaknesses.

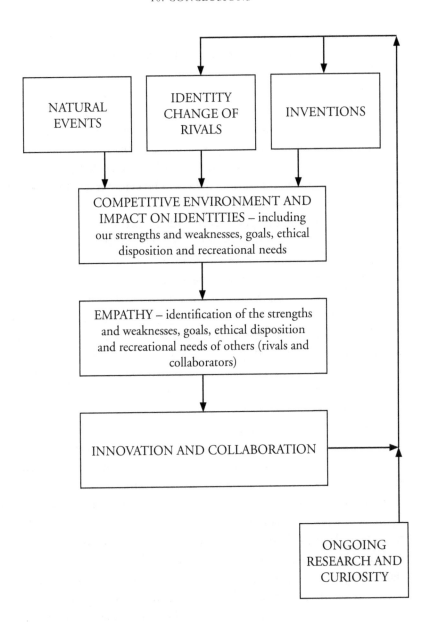

Figure 1 – A Simple Model of Social Evolution

arising through natural causes, like pandemics and global warming, has the same, quite simple, decision structure. Inevitably, those needing to change will look to existing practices and technologies that are available which they are not currently using or will soon be available. For example, how does a retailer greatly extend online trading. If that does not provide a way forward, more fundamental research may be needed, feeding into Ridley's inexorable chain of innovation. In this situation the research may need to be more directed if the crisis is to be overcome. Much will depend upon the type of crisis and how much time there will be before it has a considerable impact. The degree of Government or corporate central planning needed will also depend upon the type of crisis and urgency to overcome it. In some matters it will be vital for the Government to take action. Examples include being attacked by another country, major pandemics, or foreign seizure of national security or important company information. One understands exactly what Ridley and Wagner mean when they state that Governments and corporate head offices should aim to encourage innovation, but stay out of the innovation process itself as far as possible. However, that depends upon the type of crisis and type of innovation needed. A balance between involvement and remaining 'hands off' is needed. This is where the analytical process underlying Figure 1 to determine what to do can be very complex, despite the simple structure of the Figure.

Two caveats are needed. Figure 1 shows how *individual entities* are likely to act in the face of changes in the environment. Social evolution is, however, the result of changes in behaviours of whole populations with all members (Governments, companies , individuals, etc.) simultaneously considering their position as set out in Figure 1. The eventual social change will depend upon who wins the many competitions taking place simultaneously and how the judgement criteria are applied to a wide range of situations and actions. The model misleads in its simplicity. How society actually evolves depends upon how every individual, organisation, Government, etc. using such a model decides to act. The social evolution experienced results from a combination of these actions. Unlike the model that is a very complex process.

The second caveat concerns *when* action is taken. There may be long periods where the environment is fairly stable and in such times decision-making may well be mainly operational based mainly on experience, rather than strategic in nature. Certainly, some individuals or entities will always be researching new opportunities, but most probably are not, so long as life being experienced is acceptable. The latter will only move when a crisis is perceived. That does not mean this group is acting without reason. Why spend time worrying about something that may never happen, especially if a strategic move at the current time would create a disturbance which might lead to less desirable short-term outcomes? A balancing between probability of occurrence and cost if it does is required and it may be decided, quite rationally, not to do anything for the time being.

What Is Philosophy For?

For these last few paragraphs, I use as my heading the title of Midgley's last book: *What is philosophy for?* I stress again that I am not a philosopher by profession as she was. The main motive in writing her book was clearly to offer a critique of the deterministic, scientistic, materialistic view that she says had come to dominate the way in which we can understand the world we live in and also to object to the downgrading of the practical significance of philosophical study in some universities since the 1980s. She did not, however, argue against scientific development. Like Nagel, she hails its achievements, but says that this does not explain the whole of the universe and the place and behaviour of beings, animals and humans in it. Science and philosophy should not be in opposition. Again, like Nagel, she called for a recognition of just one reality of which both science and philosophy play their part in explain it. This seemed to resonate strongly for me, especially when I looked at work related to consciousness. On the one hand there is the work of scientists like Penrose and Crick, trying to understand how our neurological systems work while on the other there is the work of philosophers like Searle and Clark examining the question from a broader perspective. Searle calls for a blend of neurological science and biology. This suggests that to advance our understanding of consciousness we need to have scientists, philosophers and biologists working together to explore the issues involved in linking the neurological process and the biological being that produces thought. This would be a major challenge for philosophers minded to be studying consciousness and its associated concepts.

I still feel that understanding how life began and incorporated the will to survive in all living beings is basically a physical question to resolve, but philosophical thought on the subject has proved valuable already and more thinking along these lines might point scientific research in the right direction. So a current purpose of philosophy could be to examine the frontier between science and itself more thoroughly.

To justify the philosophy of the past it is only necessary to look at what philosophers have written over the last 20 or so centuries. A great deal of it has led to a clarification of confused thought for the time it was written. A great deal of it now may seem to some of little practical value, but current thought and practices stand on the shoulders of that earlier work. Our modern understanding of the Mind (still unclear), ethics, aesthetics, political philosophy and language all depend on those that struggled with these concepts in the past. Also past debates, about the need for and form of democracy for example, were very much concerned with practical issues and my text above contains a plethora of practical issues, especially at Government level, that could benefit from being addressed by philosophers. The world, however, is also never static. Both physically and socially it is continuously evolving. We are not at the end of history as was declared in support of democratic capitalism not long ago. So there will be a continuing range of key issues over which people will be puzzled. As Midgley[271] said:

> Philosophizing, in fact, is not a matter of solving one fixed set of puzzles. Instead, it involves finding the many particular ways of thinking that will be most helpful as we try to explore this constantly changing world.

Philosophy may find that matters that were once mysteries are eventually resolved by science, but there will always be different questions, especially of ethics and political philosophy, that arise as society evolves. This will never be subject to scientific resolution. Philosophy has a major part to play in

---

[271] M Midgley, op cit, 2018.

helping to understand the social evolution taking place and how to think about the problems that brings and, thereby, play a very practical part in social evolution itself. Moreover, in understanding social evolution there is the need to look at various areas of philosophy together and not treat them as watertight separate topics.

In closing, I have found the exercise thought provoking and well worth the effort even if I have not, in the process, decided to change my identity or suffered much pain in the way that, as quoted at the beginning of these notes, Isaiah Berlin thought one might. I am very aware, nevertheless, that I have merely made my own views explicit with the help of a very limited exposure to literature in philosophy and science and also that I have relied extensively on Kenny's volumes which, as he makes clear, do not address literature beyond 1975. Hence, although I have addressed some post-1975 literature in both science and philosophy, there may be huge gaps in my analysis. But it was fun – other laymen should try it! I feel better for it. I hope anyone taking this route will feel likewise.

Appendix 2
Logic

My personal understanding of Logic is that it is a process of moving from initial statements to an end conclusion through a series of connected arguments each of which necessarily follows from the previous one(s). This does not mean that the initial statements must be true or a statement of definite fact. The argument may be in the form of 'if the initial statement were true then this would follow'. Moreover, the interim statements and end conclusion need not be certainties given the initial statements. The conclusion could be in the probabilistic form 'if this initial statement holds, it is much more likely that this position will hold'. The quality of the logical analysis depends solely upon the rigour of the process of moving from initial statements through successive argument to the conclusion.

I tried to argue logically throughout this text. This is not to say, however, that I believe, like logical positivists, that all philosophical problems can be solved by logical analysis. It is fundamental to the purpose of this pamphlet to recognise that much of human behaviour is not determined by explicit logical analysis. As stated in the Introduction, behaviour is often conditioned by personal philosophies tacitly held, rather than explicitly and logically derived by the individual himself or herself. Such tacit philosophies have, almost certainly, been influenced by the environment to which the individual has been exposed. Of course, these philosophies may have been determined by logical analysis by some other influential source, but they may also be adopted as acts of faith. The word 'faith', as used here, refers to belief in the truth of something that one has not rationally and logically worked out *for oneself*. It may even just be something that one has decided to adopt as a belief in an unquestioning manner because it is convenient within one's current society or position to do so. The decision to do that might well be the result of logical analysis which concludes that it is wise in current society *to express* a particular belief, but it is not logical analysis relating to the truth of the belief itself. Nor does it mean that one necessarily holds that belief. Moreover, even if a third influential party did derive the philosophy on a logical basis, it may not have used a logic that the believer would have adopted had he or she attempted one's own analysis.

As I was exploring my own understanding of these philosophies, it was not necessary to examine the symbolic or notional representation of logical statements developed by logicians. I am aware that various systems exist, but I am not familiar with their details and so they cannot have affected the fundamental views I have (unless they were critical in deriving philosophical views of other influential persons whose views I have tacitly adopted). Hence, I have very little to say on Logic and my understanding of it is at a very general level. It was necessary, however, to express my general understanding of logic. It is only logic at the level that I perceive it to be that can be the foundation for my (logical) thinking in developing these notes.

Having said this, the place of human powers of reasoning was considered in the Section that addressed consciousness and reason.

Appendix 3
Ontology and Epistemology

Ontology addresses the question of what is Reality. Epistemology then asks how one can come to know reality given one's ontological view of it. While philosophers have argued at length about these topics over many years, my view was that I needed only a fairly basic interpretation of these terms for my purposes in constructing these notes. As regards ontology, if one regards reality in 'hard form' with solid objects and indisputable actions taken, then one is a Realist. In other words, things exist or events actually occurred which are independent of the person thinking about them. This means that one can come to know reality with an experimental approach. One will set propositions (theories) and then test them. One will collect data about this reality and through tests and associations explain how the world works. If, in contrast, one regards events and things as constructs formed by different human brains such that there is no absolutely indisputable fact, then one can only understand the world through a discursive approach. One will explore different human accounts of it which may yield some agreement, but will, almost certainly contain some shreds of difference, especially where human intention and perception is involved in social interaction.

In addressing the extent to which Realism is a valid view of the world, I am aware that Russell has argued that there is no absolute proof that the whole of life is not just a dream[272] and that our belief in an external world is instinctive rather than reflective. If this were so, it would seem to invalidate a Realist approach to seeking knowledge. There is a problem with such an argument. If all of life is only a dream, who is doing the dreaming? Does not at least someone, the dreamer, have to be real? If I dream, I, myself, cannot be a dream. I must be something real outside of the dream. Life being only a

---

[272] See Kenny, op cit, Volume 4, p 161, but I don't think that Russell himself *believed* that all life was a dream. Also, my son says that if life is all a dream, he is really impressed with himself for having 'dreamt up' the Plato he studied as a student!

dream is impossible.[273] Certainly, one can dream that one is dreaming, but, ultimately, some intelligent being must be 'doing the dreaming'.

Next, even if an independent external world did not exist and it was merely an instinctive construct, that does not mean a Realist approach to research is impossible. There may only be access to the notion of what exists through the medium of human sense-data,[274] rather than reality itself, but it is quite possible that there will some degree of agreement or, indeed, unanimity of view on some matters. The degree of agreement can be explored by a statistical methodology that might also be employed as if the world were independent and externally real. One might, of course, argue that we can never be absolutely sure whether there is any sense of agreement in sense-data because no researcher, other than the sensor, can know *exactly* what he or she is sensing. It is almost certainly true that one cannot understand the *total* sensation of another individual, but there are degrees of sensation which seem common. Take the case of pain. One may not know exactly what pain occurs when a given person is stabbed, but there does seem to be general agreement that being stabbed will be painful to most of us. It is also probable that degrees of pain can be categorised sufficiently as a real phenomenon to enable rational medical practice in treatment of pain in different circumstances.

The activity in writing these notes was, at least initially, to help me unearth (and maybe question and develop) my own views on certain main philosophical themes. This section explains my thinking on ontology and epistemology. While I have argued above that there must be something real somewhere in the universe, I accept that there is no *absolute proof* that the

---

[273] This argument follows the same line of argument as Descartes who tried to assess whether all his thoughts were simply only as true as dreams and concluded that, when he tried to think that everything he thought of was false, it was he, himself, that was doing the thinking. He, therefore, knew that he was real and could not be sceptical of all reality. He concluded, 'I think, therefore I am.' See Kenny, op cit, Volume 3, p 36. Comment on Descartes' Dualism comes later in Section 3.

[274] I use the term 'sense-data' very broadly to include sensations we have through thinking, emotional feelings, wishes and memories as well as the more obvious ones of sight, touch, taste, etc.

universe, *as I see it*, is independent and real. But, at the very least, humans do act as if a multitude of things and events are real. This may come about through the recognition of consistency in observation about things or events. For example, I can recognise common characteristics of different items called chairs and I can consistently see how they relate to tables. To the extent that there are these consistencies and I am prepared to declare them, they can be explored using 'Realist methodology' as if the objects were real. Moreover, this argument can be extended to exploring perceptions of different human beings where we can identify highly likely areas of agreement.

Acting as if something is real may not come from personal observations at all, but simply an unquestioning acceptance that something is real. This could be derived from a general conditioning by one's social context or an instinctive animal behaviour. As Wittgenstein argued that one often just acts, without an underlying theory, in a way which is in accordance with social practice or inborn animal behaviour.[275] But, while undoubtedly much, perhaps most, behaviour is like this, does this probe deeply enough? Where does this instinctive response come from? Routine animal behaviour, for example, has, without question, evolved as a means of survival. Hence, there *is* an underlying theory to animal responses. That current[276] theory may not have been thought out completely by an intelligent brain, but, through practice, it has become clear that, by in acting that way, survival can be achieved. The action is, at root, based on an evolved theory about survival.

Also, while a human may act in the way that it is customary within his or her specific society without thinking about it, that action *must* also be based on some theory constructed somewhere in the past. In such a situation one *assumes* that some effect based upon one's action is certain or at least likely, even if it is not. Hence, there is a taken-for-granted theory. This may be adopted out of unconscious habit, through instruction or through lack of awareness of the nature of the underlying phenomena. It may also be because the individual simply *wants* to assume certainty to simplify his or her life management or make it more comfortable. But it should be possible to delve

---

[275] Wittgenstein, *On Certainty*, Oxford, Blackwell, 1969.

[276] As the theory evolved, it is a truism to say that it changed over time and can still change.

further to discover the assumed certainties of social practice as though they were real and relate them to behaviours. One might, even, want to go further and try to explain how these practices became established and why they have been widely adopted. Many may not want to do this for fear of disrupting their ordered and comfortable lives if, on reflection, a previous 'certainty' became a matter of doubt. But, the very purpose of the sort of exercise that is advocated in these notes is to identify the individual philosophies that influence behaviour and this may need to involve an attempt to unearth and challenge the underlying theories of taken-for-granted philosophies. So my view is that humans may well 'just act' for large periods of time in a routine and habitual mode, but, that does not invalidate the search for a theory of why they act as they do. Indeed, occasionally, many routine actions will be reviewed especially if the social context changes which, in effect, challenges the underlying theory. Even if many of our practices are merely actions following practice within our society with no underlying theory, as Wittgenstein proposes, it is still possible for the individual to change to a different society by, for example, changing religion or lifelong political allegiance. It is unlikely that such a change is random without an underlying theory of what that change will mean to the individual.

In summary, my strong inclination is that adopting a Realist view of the universe is acceptable for many areas of enquiry, testable theories can be developed for inanimate, animal and human activities. *All* events and actions can be related to an underlying theory, albeit at some distance with effort needed to 'un-layer' the logical and evolving sequence from event back to its root cause. 'Realist research methodologies' can be employed to test most of these theories. Researching events and their determinants in physical science is an obvious example, but a 'Realist methodology' can be extended far beyond that. Realist methodology can also be employed wherever objects are considered to exist independent of *an individual's* reflection. Where social interaction occurs, a Realist research methodology may be able to reveal insights, patterns and additions to knowledge where there is significant agreement in interpretations amongst individuals. Even where there is disagreement between people about the effects of a given activity, a careful evaluation can be made examining their claims using a

Realist approach by collecting evidence and treating it statistically. There will, however, be instances where one is simply trying to gauge what happened by reference to just a few people with widely different views. Then it may only be possible to do so through a discursive, interpretive approach. It may even be preferable to take such an approach in order to get a deeper understanding of social interaction which could not be captured by numerical analysis.[277] The world has, therefore, in my view, both a Realist and interpretive dimension and one needs to fashion one's exploration methodology to fit the dimension in which one is working.

So how did this discussion influence my approach to these notes? Given what I have argued and my initial intentions in this study, one might think that a considerable insight into my own views on political philosophy, aesthetics, ethics, religion, etc. could be obtained by noting my actions and behaviour and relating that statistically to 'certain' aspects of the philosophical themes to be addressed. In principle it could. My political voting decisions could be related to political views, the paintings I have acquired might indicate my aesthetic preferences. How I have worshipped or behaved more generally might be used as evidence of religious or ethical attitudes.

This was not, however, the approach that I took. To begin with I have not recorded my decisions or actions historically in sufficiently ordered fashion to embark upon the statistical analysis required. Moreover, to undertake such an analysis over time would, perhaps, yield a misleading picture of what I believe *now*. In addition, at the outset of writing this pamphlet, much of what I think about these philosophical themes is not well defined and would be difficult to measure. Hence, the approach took was discursive based on such literature that I addressed. It was discursive in the sense of a discussion *with myself* based on contemplation and reflection. It is hoped, nevertheless, that it will be the result of logical thought which has much wider application than in just the scientific method. The two concepts must not be confused.

---

[277] This may also apply in some aspects of research in apparently 'hard' management subjects such as accounting and finance as argued quite extensively in C Tomkins and R Groves, The everyday accountant and exploring his reality, *Accounting, Organisations and Society*, No 4, 1983.

Index